Engineering Polymers

# ENGINEERING POLYMERS

Edited by

**R. W. DYSON**
Senior Lecturer in Polymer Technology
London School of Polymer Technology
Polytechnic of North London

**Blackie**
Glasgow and London

Published in the USA by
Chapman and Hall
New York

Blackie & Son Limited.
Bishopbriggs, Glasgow G64 2NZ
and
7 Leicester Place, London WC2H 7BP

Published in the USA by
Chapman and Hall
a division of Routledge, Chapman and Hall, Inc.
29 West 35th Street, New York, NY 10001-2291

© 1990 Blackie & Son Ltd
First published 1990

**British Library Cataloguing in Publication Data**

Engineering polymers.
1. Materials: Polymers
I. Dyson, R. W. (Robert William), *1942–*
620.1'92

ISBN 0-216-92678-5


**Library of Congress Cataloging-in-Publication Data**

Engineering polymers/edited by R. W. Dyson.
    p.    cm.
Bibliography: p.
Includes index.
ISBN 0-412-02081-5 (Chapman and Hall)
1. Polymers.  2. Engineering—Materials.    I. Dyson, R. W. (Robert
William), 1942–
TA455.P58E53    1990
620.1'92—dc20                                                    89-15811
                                                                      CIP

Filmset by Advanced Filmsetters (Glasgow) Ltd
Printed in Great Britain by Thomson Litho Ltd, East Kilbride, Scotland

# Contributors

**M. S. M. Alger**    London School of Polymer Technology,
The Polytechnic of North London,
Holloway, London N7 8DB, UK

**R. W. Dyson**    London School of Polymer Technology,
The Polytechnic of North London,
Holloway, London N7 8DB, UK

**J. D. Fox**    London School of Polymer Technology,
The Polytechnic of North London,
Holloway, London N7 8DB, UK

**K. S. Lee**    London School of Polymer Technology,
The Polytechnic of North London,
Holloway, London N7 8DB, UK

**R. G. Pearson**    London School of Polymer Technology,
The Polytechnic of North London,
Holloway, London N7 8DB, UK

**S. V. Wolfe**    London School of Polymer Technology
The Polytechnic of North London,
Holloway, London N7 8DB, UK

# Preface

In a material context, the word engineering evokes ideas of design, manufacture and use of materials. It can be argued that all articles made from polymers are designed and manufactured with a particular end-use in mind, and therefore that all polymers are—by definition—engineering materials. This is undoubtedly true, but the term engineering polymer is usually taken to refer to a polymeric material with properties which have been engineered by design, to produce a material with enhanced or optimised properties to meet specific end-use requirements. In this book, the term engineering polymer includes any polymeric material which has been designed and produced to meet the requirements of a specific product or range of products within a given area of use.

In recent years, certain areas have demanded not only greater use of polymeric materials but also the development of polymeric materials with specific properties. Major areas include the automotive and transport industries, electrical and electronics industries, and packaging. Other areas with a significant influence on developments have been building and construction and the sports and leisure industries. To meet their requirements, a number of new polymers have been produced and are being developed. Of equal significance is the range of modifications to existing polymers to improve performance. These modifications include chemical modification, and modification by suitable compounding with other materials—both polymeric and non-polymeric.

This book discusses polymers which are used as the basis of materials in engineering applications. Although he will find it useful, this is not aimed at the expert, but rather at those who wish to gain a general appreciation of some of the polymeric materials currently in use as engineering materials. It is hoped that this book will be useful both to postgraduate and undergraduate students—of chemistry, materials technology and engineering—and to those working in industry and commerce whose work directly or indirectly requires knowledge of polymeric materials.

R.W.D.

## Acknowledgements

The authors wish to acknowledge the help given by the following individuals in preparing the material for this book: M. Barratt, Courtaulds Composite Technologies,

Coventry; A. Barret, LSPT, London; R. Doctor, Du Pont Ltd, Hemel Hempstead; I. Dyson, Peacock Printers, Berkhamsted; M. C. Dyson, West Herts. Ambulance Service, St Albans; G. Edwards, Marley Foam Ltd, Maidstone; T. Gray, Bordon Chemicals, Southampton; S. Last, Westland Helicopters Ltd, Yeovil; N. Morys, Owens-Corning Fibreglas (UK) Ltd, Ascot; M. R. Neville, ICI, Wilton; E. Saph, ICI, Welwyn Garden City; K. Scobie, Courtaulds Composite Technologies, Coventry; D. R. Tetlow, BNL Ltd, Knaresborough; and S. Tilling, Peter Tilling Plastics, Wembley.

# Abbreviations

| | |
|---|---|
| ABS | acrylonitrile–butadiene–styrene |
| ASA | acrylonitrile–styrene–acrylate |
| ATH | alumina trihydrate |
| AZBN | azo–bis–isobutyronitrile |
| BMC | bulk moulding compound |
| CBS | N-cyclohexylbenzthiazyl sulphenamide |
| CF | carbon fibre |
| CFC | chlorofluorocarbon |
| CHP | cyclohexane peroxide |
| CNC | computerised numerical control |
| CPET | crystalline polyethyleneterephthalate |
| CR | chloroprene rubber (polychloroprene) |
| CSM | chopped strand mat |
| CTI | critical temperature index |
| DMC | dough moulding compound |
| DVNR | dynamically vulcanised natural rubber |
| EPDM | ethylene–propylene–diene monomer (elastomer) |
| EPR | ethylene propylene rubber |
| EV | efficient vulcanisation |
| EVA | ethylene vinyl acetate |
| EVOH | ethylene vinyl alcohol |
| FDA | Federal Drug Administration |
| FKM | fluoroelastomer |
| FRP | fibre reinforced polyester/plastic |
| GF | glass fibre |
| GMT | glass mat thermoplastic |
| GRP | glass reinforced polyester |
| HDPE | high density polyethylene |
| HDT | heat distortion temperature (ASTM D648) |
| HET | hexachloroendomethyleneterephthalic (acid/anhydride) |
| HIPS | high impact polystyrene (toughened polystyrene) |
| HM | high modulus |
| HNBR | hydrogenated NBR |
| HS | high strength |
| HSMC | high strength sheet moulding compound |
| HTA | high temperature amorphous |
| IBC | internal bubble cooling |
| IM | intermediate modulus |
| IPA | isopropyl alcohol |
| IPPD | N-isopropyl,N′-phenyl,p-phenylene diamine |
| LCA | loss of coolant accident |

| | |
|---|---|
| LDPE | low density polyethylene |
| LLDPE | linear low density polyethylene |
| LOI | limiting oxygen index |
| MBI | 2-mercaptobenzimidazole |
| MBS | methacrylate–butadiene–styrene |
| MD | machine direction |
| MDI | methylene di-phenyl isocyanate (di-phenylmethane di-isocyanate) |
| MEK | methyl ethyl ketone |
| MEKP | methyl ethyl ketone peroxide |
| MFR = MFI | melt flow rate/index |
| MQ | dimethyl siloxane |
| MRPRA | Malaysian Rubber Producers Research Association |
| NBR | nitrile rubber (acrylonitrile butadiene rubber) |
| NR | natural rubber |
| OPP | orientated polypropylene |
| PA | polyamide |
| PAN | polyacrylonitrile |
| PBT | polybutylene terephthalate |
| PC | polycarbonate |
| PCL | polycaprolactone |
| PE | polyethylene |
| PEEK | polyetheretherketone |
| PEK | polyetherketone |
| PET | polyethylene terephthalate |
| phr | parts per hundred parts of rubber |
| PIR | polyisocyanurate rigid (foam) |
| PP | polypropylene |
| PPE | polyphenylene ether (PPO) |
| pphr | parts per hundred resin |
| PPO | polyphenylene oxide (PPE) |
| PPS | polyphenylenesulphide |
| PS | polystyrene |
| PU | polyurethane |
| PVC | polyvinyl chloride |
| PVDC | polyvinylidene chloride |
| RIM | reaction injection moulding |
| RTM | resin transfer moulding |
| SAN | styrene acrylonitrile (copolymer) |
| SBR | styrene butadiene rubber |
| SBS | styrene–butadiene–styrene (block copolymer) |
| SEBS | styrene–ethylene–butylene–styrene |
| SF | self skinned foam |
| SIS | styrene–isoprene–styrene |
| SMA | styrene maleic anhydride |
| SMC | sheet moulding compound |
| TD | transverse direction |
| TDI | toluene di-isocyanate |
| TGDDM | tetraglycidyldiaminomethane |

| | |
|---|---|
| TPE | thermoplastic elastomer |
| TPO | thermoplastic olefine (rubber) |
| TPR | thermoplastic rubber |
| TPU | thermoplastic urethane (rubber) |
| TPV | thermoplastic vulcanisate |
| UV | ultra-violet |
| VA | vinyl acetate |
| VMQ | vinyl modified dimethyl siloxane |
| XLPE | cross-linked polyethylene |

# Trade names

| | | |
|---|---|---|
| Alcryn | EVA/chlorinated PE alloy | Du Pont |
| Arylon | polyarylate | Du Pont |
| Ardel | polyarylate | Union Carbide |
| Arnitel | polyester TPE | Akzo |
| Asaprene | styrenic TPE | Asahi |
| Azdel | glass mat thermoplastic | Azdel Inc |
| Azloy | glass mat thermoplastic | Azdel Inc |
| Azmet | glass mat thermoplastic | Azdel Inc |
| Bayblend | polycarbonate/ABS blend | Bayer |
| Cadon | polystyrene/SMA blend | Monsanto |
| Cariflex TR | styrenic TPE | Shell |
| Caprolan | thermoplastic urethane | Elastogran |
| Cycolac | polycarbonate/ABS blend | General Electric |
| Cytor | thermoplastic urethane | Cyanamid |
| Desmopan | thermoplastic urethane | Bayer |
| Dutral | TPO elastomer | Montedison |
| Dutral FLX | TPO/TPV elastomer | Montedison |
| Dutralene | TPO elastomer | Himont |
| Dutrex | aromatic petroleum oil | Shell |
| Elastollan | thermoplastic urethane | Elastogran |
| Elexar | styrenic TPE | Shell |
| Estane | thermoplastic urethane | Goodrich |
| Estamid | polyamide TPE | Dow |
| Europrene Sol T | styrenic TPE | Enichem |
| Exxelar | functionalised polyethylene | Exxon |
| Finaprene | radial SB elastomer | Petrofina |
| Flectol | polymerised hydroquinoline | Bayer |
| Gaflex | polyester TPE | Gaf |
| Geolast | TPO/TPV elastomer | Monsanto |
| Grilamid ELT | polyamide TPE | EMS-Chemie |
| Grilamid ELX | polyamide TPE | EMS-Chemie |
| Grilamid TR | aromatic polyamide | EMS-Chemie |
| Hypalon | chlorosulphonated PE | Du Pont |
| Hytrel | polyester TPE | Du Pont |

| Ixef | aromatic polyamide | Solvay |
| Jectothane | thermoplastic urethane | Dunlop |
| Keltan TP | TPO elastomer | DSM |
| Kelprox | TPO/TPV elastomer | DSM |
| Kerimid | bis-maleimide polyimide | Rhone-Poulenc |
| Kevlar | aramid fibre | Du Pont |
| Kraton | styrenic TPE | Shell |
| K-resin | SB star block copolymer | Phillips |
| Lebaflex | TPO elastomer | Bayer |
| Makroblend | polycarbonate/PBT blend | Bayer |
| Maranyl | polyamide | ICI |
| Nomex | aramid fibre | Du Pont |
| Norsophen | phenolic resin | Orkem |
| Lomod | polyester TPE | General Electric |
| Noryl | polyphenylene oxide blend | General Electric |
| Noryl GTX | PPO/nylon blend | General Electric |
| Orgalloy | nylon/polypropylene blend | Atochem |
| Orthane | thermoplastic urethane | Ohio |
| Paraloid EXL | functionalised acrylic polymer | Rohm & Haas |
| Pebax | polyamide TPE | Atochem |
| Pelprene | polyester TPE | Toyobo |
| Pellethane | polyester TPE | Dow |
| Pibiflex | polyester TPE | Montedison |
| Plastothane | thermoplastic urethane | Thiokol |
| Polystal | glass mat thermoset | Bayer |
| Pulse | polycarbonate/ABS | Dow |
| Q-thane | thermoplastic urethane | Quinn |
| Riteflex | polyester TPE | Hoechst-Celanese |
| Roylar | thermoplastic urethane | Uni-Royal |
| Rucothane | thermoplastic urethane | Hooker |
| Rynite | polyester | Du Pont |
| Ryton | polyphenylene sulphide | Phillips |
| Santoprene | TPO/TPV elastomer | Monsanto |
| Skybond 700 | polyimide | Monsanto |
| Solprene | SB star block elastomer | Phillips |
| Somel | TPO elastomer | Du Pont |
| Stanyl | polyamide 4.6 | DSM |
| Telcar | TPO elastomer | Goodrich |
| Terblend | polycarbonate/ABS blend | BASF |
| Texin | thermoplastic urethane | Mobay |
| Therban | hydrogenated nitrile rubber | Bayer |
| Torlon | polyamideimide | Amoco |
| Trefsin | TPO/TPV elastomer | Exxon |
| Triax | nylon/ABS blend | Monsanto |
| Trogamid T | aromatic polyamide | Dynamit Nobel |
| Tufprene | styrenic TPE | Asahi |
| Ultem | polyetherimide | General Electric |
| Ultrablend | polycarbonate/PBT blend | BASF |

| Ultranyl | PPO/nylon blend | BASF |
| Uneprene | TPO elastomer | ISR |
| Verton | long fibre thermoplastic | ICI |
| Vestolene EM | TPO elastomer | Huls |
| Victrex | engineering thermoplastics | ICI |
| Vistaflex | TPO elastomer | Exxon |
| Xenoy | polycarbonate/PBT blend | General Electric |
| Zytel | polyamide | Du Pont |

# Contents

## 5 Long fibre reinforced thermoset composites      101
R. W. DYSON

## 6 Co-extruded films and containers      138
J. D. FOX

# 7 Polymers in telecommunications and power transmission 164
S. V. WOLFE

# 1 Thermoplastic composites

M. S. M. ALGER *and* R. W. DYSON

## 1.1 Introduction

In recent years, there has been a significant increase in the use of plastics materials in many areas of engineering which had previously been dominated by non-polymeric materials, especially metals. Thermoplastic polymers allow the production of complex shapes, principally by injection moulding, with relative ease and little or no finishing requirements. Developments in the technology of injection moulding machines, especially their control systems, have enabled products to be made to tight specifications and with great consistency over large runs (tens of thousands of components). Additionally, thermoplastics allow inserts to be moulded in readily and allow several components to be welded together with speed and precision, using a number of very effective techniques such as friction welding or ultrasonic welding. Products can be self-coloured by incorporating pigments or dyes, either prior to or at the moulding stage. Alternatively, surface colouration can be obtained by spray-painting, perhaps even with decorative effects through the use of suitable masking. Surface metallisation can be achieved by vacuum techniques, among others, and a recent development has been the in-mould painting technique whereby the mould surface is sprayed with paint which adheres to the solidified plastic moulding. It is the mechanical properties, however, that generally determine the end-use of a thermoplastic polymer in most applications.

The ideal thermoplastic for engineering applications will have the following attributes:

strength (tensile, compressive and flexural);
high modulus (stiffness, especially flexural);
impact resistance;
fatigue resistance;
creep resistance;
heat resistance (to degradation and softening);
chemical stability (including UV);
dimensional stability (which implies low water absorption).

In addition, it should be easy to process and have low mould shrinkage.

Unfortunately it is difficult to produce a polymer which maximises all of these requirements because the factors which enhance some properties will

**Table 1.1** Typical properties of engineering polymers

| | Specific gravity | Tensile strength (MPa) | Tensile modulus (GPa) | Elongation at break (%) | Flexural strength (MPa) |
|---|---|---|---|---|---|
| Polyamide 46 | 1.18 | 40 | 1.0 | 280 | 30 |
| Polyarylate | 1.19–1.21 | 70 | 2.0–2.1 | 25– 50 | 76–83 |
| Polyetheretherketone | 1.3 | 92 | 3 –6 | 50 | 170 |
| Polyetherketone | 1.3 | 105 | 4 | 5 | |
| Polyethersulphone | 1.37 | 84 | 2.4 | 40– 80 | 129 |
| Polyetherimide | 1.27 | 105 | 2.8 | 60 | 145 |
| Polysulfone | 1.24 | 70 | 2.5 | 50–100 | 108 |
| Victrex HTA | 1.36 | 86 | 2.3 | 19 | 125 |
| Polyacetal | 1.42 | 63–72 | 2.6–3.1 | 15– 75 | 91–98 |
| Polyamide 66 | 1.1 | 50–84 | 1.8–2.8 | 60–300 | 40–50 |
| Polyamide 6 | 1.13 | 70–84 | 1.0–2.5 | 90–320 | 40 |
| Polycarbonate | 1.21 | 60–65 | 2.2–2.4 | 60–100 | 95 |
| Polyethyleneterephthalate | 1.35–1.4 | 50–70 | 2.8–4.2 | 30–300 | 100+ |
| Polybutyleneterephthalate | 1.30–1.35 | 55–60 | 2 –3 | 50–300 | 100+ |
| Polypropylene | 0.91 | 28–38 | 0.9–1.4 | 50–600 | 35–55 |

diminish others. For example, performance at high temperature requires a polymer with a high glass transition temperature ($T_g$). This has the advantage of improving stiffness and creep resistance, but often the disadvantages of lowering impact resistance and reducing ease of processing. Nevertheless, the range of thermoplastic polymers has been extended over the last 10–15 years by the development and commercialisation of numerous new polymers. These include: partially aromatic polyamides (e.g. Trogamid™, Grilamid™, Ixef™), polyetherimides (e.g. Ultem™), polyamideimides (e.g. Torlon™), polyetheretherketones (e.g. Victrex PEEK™), polyetherketones (e.g. Victrex PEK™), polyamide 46 (e.g. Stanyl™), polyarylates (e.g. Arylon™, Ardel™) and a polyethersulphone related material designated Victrex HTA™. Table 1.1 summarises the properties of these polymer types and gives an indication of the properties of other engineering polymers for comparison.

### 1.1.1 The need for additives

Despite the undoubted general excellence of many polymers, there remains the need to modify and regulate the properties of any one polymer to overcome specific deficiencies and make it more suitable for a particular application. The use of polymers at all levels of engineering can be extended by using additives, in amounts which range from 0.1% to over 40%. Additives

**Table 1.1** (*cont'd*)

| Notched Izod impact (kJ/m²) | HDT (1.82 MPa) (°C) | Thermal expansion (mm/mm °C × 10⁵) | Mould shrinkage (%) | Water absorption (equilibrium, 50 RH) (%) | $T_g$ (°C) | $T_m$ (°C) |
|---|---|---|---|---|---|---|
| 40       | 160     | 7.5      | 1.5 –2.4  | 3.7        | —    | 295 |
| 17 –23   | 155–175 | 5.5– 6.2 | 0.01–0.2  | 0.1 –0.3   | —    | —   |
| 6.7      | 160     | 5        | 1.1       | 0.15–0.2   | 143  | 334 |
| 7.0      | 186     | 5.7      | 0.6       | 0.18       | 162  | 373 |
| 6.0      | 200     | 5.5      | 0.7       | 1.25       | 190  | —   |
| 2.4– 4.0 | 200     | 5.6      | 0.6       | 0.25       | 216  | —   |
| 7.0      | 174     | 5.6      | 0.7       | —          | 190  | —   |
| 12.3     | 234     | 5.4      | 0.8       | 1.3        | 260  | —   |
| 3 –10    | 90–125  | 6 –10    | 1.8 –2.5  | 0.02–0.4   | –65  | 170 |
| 4 –8     | 75      | 8 –13    | 1 –2      | >2.5       | 55   | 260 |
| 10 –12   | 70      | 8 –13    | 0.8 –1.5  | 1.3 –2.5   | 30   | 215 |
| 64       | 132     | 7 – 8    | 0.5 –0.8  | 0.15–0.35  | 145  | —   |
| 1 – 3    | 40– 90  | 6 – 9    | 2 –2.5    | 0.1 –0.2   | 75   | 260 |
| 2 – 4    | 50– 85  | 6 – 9    | 1.5 –2.0  | 0.08–0.09  | 50   | 225 |
| 1 –16    | 50– 60  | 11 –15   | 1.5 –2.5  | <0.01      | –18  | 170 |

such as UV stabilisers, antioxidants and fire retardants are required with many polymers to enhance their stability in service.

It is the modification of mechanical and related properties which is the principal concern of this chapter. In general terms, modifications can be considered in three categories:

(i) the addition of fibres (usually glass) to improve heat resistance, rigidity and creep resistance;

(ii) the addition of inorganic particulate fillers to enhance dimensional stability;

(iii) the addition of rubbery components to improve impact resistance and low temperature performance.

There are additional benefits from the presence of these additives, but other properties may be downgraded. A particular grade of plastic will therefore be a carefully selected blend of polymer and additives in appropriate quantities to give an optimum set of properties for an application.

The main reason why so much work has gone into the development of modified thermoplastics rather than the creation of new polymers is largely cost. It is very much cheaper to take existing polymers and develop composite systems based upon these, than it is to develop new polymers. Commercial production of composites presents no real problem since additives can be compounded with the base polymer at high rates (up to 5 tonnes/h) using modern, twin-screw compounding extruders for example.

**Figure 1.1** Bearings moulded in polyacetal (BNL Ltd, Knaresborough).

Although the initial demand was to modify the properties of the recognised engineering thermoplastics, there have been increased efforts in recent years to upgrade the so-called commodity plastics which are polymers and copolymers based on olefines, vinyl chloride and styrene. A reason for this is that the tonnage production and end-use of these polymers is over 90% of all thermoplastics, and consequently their cost is considerably less than that of the cheapest of the recognised engineering plastics (acetals and nylons). Variously modified forms of polypropylene (PP), polyvinyl chloride (PVC) and acrylonitrile–butadiene–styrene (ABS) are now used in many engineering applications.

As well as the use of additives, considerable effort has gone into development of blends and alloys of polymers to obtain desirable properties. In many instances, property modifications can be achieved only by blending. An example is the range of polycarbonate alloys which has been developed for the automotive industry to overcome the detrimental effect of environmental conditions on impact resistance. These blends and alloys are also subject to modifications with fibres, inorganic fillers and rubbers.

Several areas of industry have prompted the increase in the use of modified thermoplastic polymers, but none more so than the automotive industry—in Europe in 1987 this used over 600 000 tonnes of thermoplastics, of which about 90 000 tonnes were glass-reinforced grades. The demand for reduced vehicle weight to help to reduce fuel consumption, the need for increased safety and for improved ease of component production and assembly have all contributed to the increased demands upon polymers. Applications

**Figure 1.2** Part of a roller-skate moulded in a rubber-modified glass-filled grade of Du Pont's Rynite™ (moulded by Tratt Plastics, Basingstoke).

include: interior and exterior components, such as panels, trims, grilles, fascias, knobs and handles; under-bonnet components, such as distributor caps, radiators, fans, battery trays, oil and water pumps; and other components such as fuel-tanks, foot pedals, automatic transmission selectors, instrument gears and boot locks. The first plastic component for use inside an engine has been announced by a group of American companies. It is a camshaft which is injection moulded from glass-reinforced Ryton™ polyphenylenesulphide around a hollow steel core. Weight and cost are estimated to be up to half those of conventional shafts with a reduction in component manufacture time from hours to minutes. Other general industrial uses include housings for machinery and tools, tools and medical equipment and bearings (Figure 1.1). The sports and leisure industries have also made significant use of modified thermoplastics in the manufacture of items such as cycle wheels and frames and roller-skates (Figure 1.2). The electrical industries are using modified thermoplastics for equipment housings (switches, connectors, meters and motors), whilst the electronics industry is moving away from epoxide-based circuit boards to thermoplastic ones. The demand is there and it is likely to increase.

## 1.2 Fibre reinforcement

### 1.2.1 General

Fibres are able to reinforce a weaker polymer matrix if they themselves are stronger and of higher modulus and provided that the polymer matrix adheres to the fibre. The most commonly used fibre is E-glass, but the more expensive carbon fibres are increasing in use for special purposes (see section 5.3.3). The fibres are treated with agents to improve wetting by the polymer and thereby improve adhesion. Some agents also act as coupling agents to bind the fibre more firmly to the polymer, further improving adhesion. Adhesion is of great importance in injection and extrusion grades of fibre-reinforced thermoplastics because in most cases the fibres used are short (0.3–0.6 mm) and of less than the critical fibre length for maximum stress transfer (2–5 mm). Without adhesion, the fibre ends would not be able to resist the shear forces between polymer and fibre when the component is stressed and the composite would fail at much lower applied stress levels than if the fibre were absent (see 5.3.1). Adhesion is never 100% efficient and the reinforcement obtained with short fibres is never as good as when long fibres are used. Nevertheless, significant improvements in strength and stiffness can be achieved.

The fibres are most commonly incorporated into the polymer melt in a twin-screw extruder fed by a metered mixture of fibre and polymer granules. The fibres fed to the machine are several millimetres in length but are broken down by mechanical forces during the mixing process. Injection moulding causes relatively little further breakdown of the fibre length if flow pathways are smooth and reasonably sized. Measurements have shown that the average fibre length is reduced by about 70% by the injection moulding process. Many moulders use reclaimed material at about 10% with virgin material and produce mouldings with little or no loss in properties compared with those moulded from virgin polymer.

The stronger, higher modulus carbon fibres give better reinforcement in terms of strength and stiffness than glass fibres, but at considerably greater cost. However, melt flow is generally easier with carbon fibres compared with glass fibre at the same loading. Aramid fibres are also used to impart toughness.

### 1.2.2 Reinforcement

Several equations have been derived from the theory of mixing to account for tensile strength and modulus of short fibre composites. For example, the modulus is given by the Lewis–Nielsen modification of the Halpin–Tsai equation

$$E_c = \frac{E_r(1 + 2AB\phi_f)}{1 - B\psi\phi_f} \tag{1.1}$$

where

$$B = \frac{(E_f/E_r) - 1}{(E_f/E_r) + 2A}$$

and

$$\psi = 1 + \frac{(1-V_r)\phi_f}{2V_r}$$

and $E_c$, $E_r$, $E_f$ are the moduli of composite, resin matrix and fibre respectively, $\phi_f$ is the volume fraction of the fibre, $A$ is the aspect ratio, and $\psi$ is the maximum packing fraction.

Strength is given by Kelly's equation

$$\sigma_c = \eta A \tau_r \phi_f + \sigma_r(1-\phi_f) \qquad (1.2)$$

where $\sigma_c$ is the composite breaking stress, $\sigma_r$ is the stress on the resin matrix at the strain at which failure occurs, $\tau_r$ is the interfacial shear stress which is that of the matrix polymer if adhesion is 100% effective and $\eta$ is an orientation

**Table 1.2** The effect of glass (G) and carbon (C) fibres on the mechanical properties of amorphous and semi-crystalline polymers (y = yield)

| Polymer | Reinforcement | Tensile strength (MPa) | Elongation at break (%) | Tensile modulus (GPa) | Flexural strength (MPa) | Flexural modulus (GPa) |
|---|---|---|---|---|---|---|
| **SEMI-CRYSTALLINE** | | | | | | |
| Polybutyleneterephthalate | none | 57y | 50–300 | 1.96 | 98 | 2.8 |
| | 30% G | 126 | 3 | 9.1 | 193 | 8.4 |
| | 30% C | 160 | 1.5 | 24.5 | 220 | 17.5 |
| Polypropylene | none | 37y | 100–600 | 1.2 | 49 | 1.5 |
| | 40% G | 82 | 3 | 9.1 | 107 | 7.0 |
| | 30% C | 48 | 0.5 | 11.9 | 63 | 11.3 |
| Polyetherketone | none | 105 | 5 | 4 | — | 3.7 |
| | 30% G | 170 | 4 | 10.5 | — | 9.0 |
| | 30% C | 225 | 3 | — | — | 17.9 |
| Polyetheretherketone | none | 92y | 50 | — | 170 | 3.7 |
| | 30% G | 157 | 2.2 | — | 233 | 10.3 |
| | 30% C | 208 | 1.3 | — | 318 | 13 |
| **AMORPHOUS** | | | | | | |
| Polyethersulphone | none | 84y | 40–80 | — | 129 | 2.6 |
| | 30% G | 104 | 3 | — | 190 | 8.4 |
| | 30% C | 196 | 2 | 15 | 259 | 17.5 |
| Victrex HTA | none | 86 | 19 | — | 125 | 2.5 |
| | 30% G | 134 | 4 | — | 204 | 8.5 |
| Polycarbonate | none | 63 | 110 | 2.4 | 95 | 2.4 |
| | 30% G | 133 | 4 | 8.8 | 161 | 7.7 |
| | 30% C | 168 | 3 | 15 | 245 | 13.3 |
| ABS (rigid) | none | 40 | 5 – 25 | 2.4 | 84 | 2.6 |
| | 30% G | 77 | 3 | 5.2 | 101 | 4.9 |

factor. In practice, such equations are limited to small strains and linear viscoelastic behaviour.

The degree of reinforcement depends on several factors, including whether or not the polymer can crystallise and if so, the amount of crystallinity developed. Table 1.2 gives representative figures for typical amorphous and semi-crystalline polymers. Carbon fibres are more efficient at reinforcement than glass fibres for the same loading, as would be expected from their higher strength and modulus. Additionally, the carbon fibre composites have a lower density than glass fibre composites with the same degree of reinforcement. Semi-crystalline polymers are more efficiently reinforced than are amorphous polymers. This is in part due to the fact that the fibres act as nucleation sites for crystallisation and the fibre becomes surrounded by a microcrystalline structure which binds the fibre more firmly to the polymer, as well as improving modulus in its own right. It should be noted that the modulus, especially flexural modulus, is enhanced more than strength. A further factor is that as the amount of crystallinity increases, so does the degree of reinforcement. The figures for PEEK and PEK, which are approximately 35% crystalline, should be compared with the more crystalline polyesters.

The amount of moisture absorbed by the polymer also affects the reinforcement values. Water acts as a plasticiser and decreases strength and stiffness, but increases toughness. The incorporation of low moisture-absorbing fibres produces a composite with lower water absorption than the base polymer. Polymers with relatively high water absorption (e.g. nylons) therefore benefit in two ways from the addition of fibre and this is of significance in determining properties in service conditions (Table 1.3).

**Table 1.3** Effect of moisture and glass fibre on mechanical properties of polyamides

|  |  | Tensile strength (MPa) | Elongation at break (%) | Tensile modulus (GPa) | Flexural strength (MPa) | Flexural modulus (GPa) | Water absorption (equil. at 50% RH) (%) |
|---|---|---|---|---|---|---|---|
| Nylon 6 | dry | 82(y) | 30–100 | 2.7 | 110 | 2.73 | 2 –3 |
|  | cond. | 52(y) | 300 | 0.7 | 41 | 0.98 |  |
| 30% GF nylon 6 | dry | 168(b) | 3– 6 | 10.2 | 231 | 9.1 | 1.5 |
|  | cond. | 112(b) | 6– 7 | 5.6 | 147 | 5.6 |  |
| Nylon 46 | dry | 100(y) | 30 | 3 | 150 | 3.2 | 3.7 |
|  | cond. | 40(y) | 280 | 1 | 50 | 1.0 |  |
| 30% GF nylon 46 | dry | 210(b) | 4 | 9.2 | 300 | 8.5 | 2.6 |
|  | cond. | 120(b) | 8 | 4.5 | 190 | 4.6 |  |

y = yield; b = break; cond. = conditioned.

**Table 1.4** Effect of glass fibre on the heat distortion temperature (HDT) at 1.81 MPa load. All values are in °C

| Polymer | HDT-unfilled | HDT-30% GF | $T_g$ | $T_m$ |
|---|---|---|---|---|
| SEMI-CRYSTALLINE POLYMERS | | | | |
| Polyetherketone | 186 | 358 | 162 | 373 |
| Polyetheretherketone | 160 | 315 | 143 | 334 |
| Polyamide 46 | 160 | 285 | — | 295 |
| Polyamide 66 | 75 | 250 | 55 | 260 |
| Polyamide 6 | 66–80 | 220 | — | 225 |
| Polybutylene terephthalate | 50–85 | 220 | — | 230 |
| Polyethylene terephthalate | 41 | 220 | 75 | 265 |
| Polyacetal | 124 | 164 | −65 | 170 |
| AMORPHOUS POLYMERS | | | | |
| Victrex HTA | 234 | 252 | 260 | |
| Polyethersulphone | 203 | 216 | 220 | |
| Polysulphone | 174 | 177 | 190 | |
| Polycarbonate | 132 | 146 | 150 | |

The use of fibres increases the softening temperature of a polymer and the result is approximately the same whether glass or carbon is used. The effect is greater with semi-crystalline polymers than with amorphous polymers where the gain is typically 10°–20°C. This is because with amorphous polymer, softening is governed by $T_g$ and softening occurs at about 20°C below $T_g$ for the unmodified polymer. The temperature at which semi-crystalline polymers soften is determined by the melting point ($T_m$), melting range and amount of crystallinity as well as $T_g$. High softening points are obtained with a high $T_m$, narrow melting range and high percentage crystallinity. The addition of fibres essentially replaces the amorphous polymer and the greatest effects are obtained in semi-crystalline polymers of moderate crystallinity (Table 1.4).

Creep is continuous deformation under constant load and is due to molecular mobility, principally in amorphous polymer. Creep is generally, but not always, associated with $T_g$ but certainly it becomes more significant above $T_g$. The addition of fibres impedes the molecular mobility and consequently the creep resistance is increased. The effect of fibre on creep resistance is generally greater with amorphous polymer, as crystalline polymer will inhibit creep anyway. In either case, creep is reduced at higher temperatures (Figure 1.3).

Fibres do little to improve impact resistance and in many instances the impact resistance is reduced (Table 1.5). The fibre ends act as stress concentration points and if adhesion is relatively poor, there is little to impede the propagation of a crack through the polymer matrix. Impact resistance can be improved by using longer fibres and improving adhesion by means of coupling agents. The most significant gains in impact resistance are obtained by using rubber modifiers (section 1.6.4).

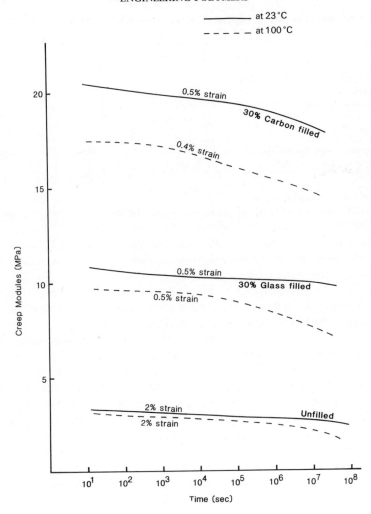

**Figure 1.3** Creep modulus curves for Victrex PEEK™ materials.

### 1.2.3 Dimensional stability

An important factor in using thermoplastics in engineering applications is dimensional stability, which is the resistance to dimensional change in service. These changes can occur because of changes in temperature, changes in humidity, creep and post-mould shrinking due to further crystallisation. Fibres have significantly lower thermal expansion coefficients (glass is $8 \times 10^{-6}$ mm/mm K) than polymers ($50$–$200 \times 10^{-6}$ mm/mm K) and consequently, fibre-reinforced plastics show greater dimensional stability to temperature changes than unreinforced polymer. Similarly, water absorption

**Table 1.5** Notched Izod impact strengths ($kJ/m^2$) of glass-reinforced polymers

|  | Unreinforced | 30% glass fibre |
|---|---|---|
| Polyethersulphone | 11.6 | 13.1 |
| Polyetheretherketone | 12.8 | 14.8 |
| Polyetherketone | 7.0 | 9.0 |
| Polyamide 46 | 40 (10)* | 19 (11)* |
| Polycarbonate | 67 | 8 |
| Polybutylene terephthalate | 4 | 6 |
| Polypropylene | 4 | 6 |

* conditioned (dry).

characteristics of composites are lower than the base polymer because the fibres absorb little moisture compared with the polymers.

An undesirable effect of using fibres is orientation, which leads to anisotropy in mouldings. Usually, thermal expansion is greater in the transverse direction than in the flow direction and the difference increases with the degree of orientation. An effect of this is that the differential expansion can set up internal stresses on heating, leading to warping of the product which is often a greater problem than with unreinforced polymer.

The use of fibres tends to mar the surface finish, especially at high fibre contents. The most common result is a matt rather than a gloss finish. This can be overcome by using a two-stage injection process whereby unfilled polymer is injected into a less than full size mould in the first stage, after which the mould is increased to full size and the reinforced polymer is injected in the second stage. The result is a sandwich with a reinforced core and skins with a good surface finish and with the additional benefit of improved impact resistance. Alternatively, the process can be reversed to produce mouldings with reinforced skins round an unreinforced core. An advantage of this type of moulding is that high modulus components can be produced at reduced cost compared with wholly reinforced mouldings.

### 1.2.4 Processing considerations

The use of fibre reinforcements produces higher melt viscosities at a given shear rate. This necessitates the use of higher melt temperatures for processing and higher injection pressures may also be required. Carbon fibres have less effect than glass fibres on melt flow. The lower heat capacities of glass and carbon means that the heating requirements to obtain a suitable melt, and more importantly, the heat removal requirements of fibre-reinforced mouldings are often less than with unreinforced polymer.

The incorporation of fibres reduces mould shrinkage because of lower thermal expansion coefficients and, in the case of semi-crystalline polymers, also because of the reduction in loss of volume on crystallisation. The effect is therefore more marked with semi-crystalline polymers. Although mould shrinkage is reduced, fibre orientation leads to differential shrinkage, that in the flow direction being significantly less than that in the transverse direction. For example, 30% GF PEEK has shrinkages of about 0.7% in the flow direction and 1.4% in the transverse direction, dependent upon the moulding conditions.

The biggest disadvantage to the moulder in using fibres is abrasive wear on machinery and moulds, with glass fibres being appreciably more abrasive than carbon. The screw is particularly prone to damage, as are components such as check-valves which have been known to disappear completely. Screw damage can be reduced by using low screw speeds, which also minimise fibre degradation. Wear in the mould itself leads to inconsistencies in moulding dimensions during a production run. Parts need to be replaced and moulding costs are thereby increased.

### 1.2.5  Glass microspheres

Glass microspheres, both solid and hollow, offer some advantages over glass fibres. As they are spherical, they have no orientation effects and any anistropy in a composite moulding results from the polymer itself; processability is better, and the surface finish of the moulding can be as good as when the polymer alone is used provided that the spheres are sufficiently small. Typically, solid spheres are about 30 μm in diameter and hollow spheres are about 70 μm. Solid spheres are the more common at present, despite the advantage offered by hollow spheres of lower density. The spheres are usually of A-glass because the rheological properties of molten A-glass allow the formation of spheres more easily than E-glass.

Because the aspect ratio of a sphere is unity, the reinforcing effect is much less than if fibres are used and it is essential that appropriate coupling agents are used to maximise reinforcement. The lesser reinforcement is compensated for to some extent by the ability to use microspheres at higher loadings (40–50%) than is usual with fibres. Mixtures of microspheres and fibres can be used to optimise properties. Microspheres are most commonly used with nylons and Table 1.6 gives comparative properties of various reinforcements with nylon 66.

## 1.3  Long fibre reinforcement

### 1.3.1  Long fibre reinforced thermoplastics

A recent development has been the introduction of thermoplastic polymers reinforced with longer than normal fibres under the name Verton™. The fibre (glass, carbon or aramid) is fed into the extruder at the head in the manner of wire coating to avoid breakdown of the fibre by the extruder screw. The

**Table 1.6** Effect of glass reinforcements on the properties of dry nylon 66

|  | Filler | None | 40% glass spheres | 33% glass fibre | 25% bead & 15% fibre |
|---|---|---|---|---|---|
| Tensile strength | (MPa) | 80 | 99 | 196 | 161 |
| Elongation at break | (%) | 6 | 2.5 | 2.0 | 2.1 |
| Flexural modulus | (GPa) | 3.0 | 5.1 | 9.1 | 8.9 |
| Izod impact strength | (kJ/m²) | 4.2 | 2.5 | 8.4 | 4.2 |
| HDT (1.81 MPa) | (°C) | 71 | 74 | 250 | 208 |
| Specific gravity |  | 1.14 | 1.43 | 1.38 | 1.46 |
| Water absorption (24 h) (%) |  | 1.4 | 0.8 | 0.9 | 0.8 |

**Table 1.7** Properties of Verton long fibre reinforced nylons (figures in brackets are for water conditioned material, otherwise for dry material)

|  | Tensile strength (MPa) | Elongation at break (%) | Flexural strength (MPa) | Flexural modulus (GPa) | Notched Izod (kJ/m²) | HDT (1.81 MPa) (°C) | Expansion coefficient ($°C^{-1} \times 10^5$) | Water absorption (24 h) (%) | Density (g/cc) |
|---|---|---|---|---|---|---|---|---|---|
| **NYLON 66** | | | | | | | | | |
| 30% glass | 195(140) | 4(6) | 320(200) | 10 (6.2) | 18(25) | 255 | 4 | 0.7 | 1.37 |
| 50% glass | 230(165) | 4(6) | 400(260) | 15.8(11.2) | 27(37) | 261 | 3 | 0.4 | 1.57 |
| 40% aramid | 117 | 2.4 | 158 | 7.1 | 8.3 | 246 | — | 0.4 | 1.24 |
| **NYLON 6** | | | | | | | | | |
| 30% glass | 175 | 4 | 290 | 10 | 20 | 215 | — | 0.8 | 1.35 |
| 50% glass | 200 | 4 | 320 | 15 | 30 | 218 | — | 0.8 | 1.57 |

extrudate is cut at the die face to produce granules of 1–10 mm in length with the fibres orientated in the flow direction. If recommended mould design and process conditions are followed—sections, gates and runners are generous without sharp curves and injection and screw speeds are as low as possible— injection moulding of these granules produces reinforced products containing fibres of 1–10 mm in length which are highly orientated, and with minimal fibre attrition.

Products made using long fibres have better impact resistance and higher stiffness than the conventional fibre-reinforced mouldings (Table 1.7). Additionally, there is better retention of stiffness at high temperatures and failure under impact occurs in such a way that the failure mode is safer. Long fibres also result in products with good surface finish (because of the orientation and because there are fewer fibre ends), better dimensional stability and enhanced creep and fatigue resistance. Mould shrinkage is about 60% of conventional short fibre reinforced polymer.

In principle, any polymer can be reinforced with long fibres but at the moment the principal polymers used are the various nylons, although Verton™ grades based on most engineering thermoplastics are available. Table 1.7 gives an indication of the properties of polyamide-based Verton™ materials. These materials are currently used in many industrial and domestic appliances (gear wheels, brackets, power-tool housings, carburettor inlet manifolds), in automobiles (gear mechanisms, foot pedals, steering wheels etc.), in aerospace (anti-surge fuel flaps), sport and leisure (golf putters, windsurfer boom connectors) and electrical equipment (solder rail combs, box covers and housings).

### 1.3.2 Glass mat thermoplastics (GMT)

Another long fibre development is the use of woven or knitted mattings. Examples are the materials marketed as Azdel™, Azloy™, Azmet™ and Polystal™. The matting is impregnated with thermoplastic polymer to produce a semi-finished sheet. A blank of appropriate size is cut from the sheet, pre-heated and then compressed in a cold mould to form the product. The process is sometimes known as melt–flow stamping and it is capable of producing large components. An alternative is to place the cold GMT into a hot press, press it to shape and cool it, but the method has the disadvantage of long cycle times. Compared with compression moulding of thermosetting sheet materials (SMC), GMT materials have no long-term storage problems, require fewer post-moulding operations and their waste material can be recycled. Furthermore, components can be welded together.

Fibre contents of up to about 80% can be used and this leads not only to high mechanical strength and stiffness, but also to greater dimensional stability and heat resistance. Polypropylene-based materials, for example, can have a thermal expansion coefficient of $2.7 \times 10^{-5}$ mm/mm K and a HDT (1.8 MPa) of 165°C. Tensile strengths of 500 MPa and moduli of over 30 GPa can be obtained with appropriate engineering polymers which include a wide range of amorphous and semi-crystalline materials. Uses for these materials include automotive bumpers, under shielding, housings, steering column supports, heater housings as well as air freight containers. All of these require high strength, stiffness and impact resistance. Other areas of use or potential use include furniture, material handling pallets, containers, engineering components, electronics and sports equipment.

An alternative to impregnation of woven matting is the production of fibre-reinforced sheet by a modified paper-making process (the Radlite process). Examples of this type of sheet are Azloy-F™ and Azmet-F™. These materials have better flow characteristics than impregnated cloths, allowing complex and intricate shapes to be moulded with better control of section thickness variations. Furthermore, improved surface finish (class A) can be obtained. They are finding use as automotive exterior body components and as base materials for printed circuit boards.

## 1.4 Mineral powder fillers

### 1.4.1 Introduction

Mineral fillers used in thermoplastics are usually inorganic powders such as chalk, talc, mica and other silicates. Mineral powders have been used for many years to improve dimensional stability of moulded components. Generally, they have lower thermal expansion coefficients than polymers and most do not undergo any significant phase change in the normal temperature range experienced by polymers in service or during processing. Therefore, like the fibres discussed in section 1.2.3, mineral powder filled polymer composites have greater stability to temperature changes and have lower mould shrinkage than the unfilled polymer. Furthermore, the low aspect ratio of powder particles produces mouldings in which anisotropic effects through orientation are small or even non-existent and thus the tendency to warp with changes in temperature is reduced. Surface finish can be as good as with unfilled polymer, but depends on the amount of filler, particle size and particle dispersion. Another advantage over fibres is that material costs are often lower. This should not be taken to mean that fillers are used to cheapen the product. If they do so it is a bonus, but in most cases mineral-filled grades of a polymer are more expensive than unfilled grades and mouldings will cost more because the moulded article is heavier. Although mineral powders cause abrasive wear to moulds and machinery, it is less than that produced by glass.

### 1.4.2 Reinforcement

Until quite recently, mineral powders had little effect on strength properties and in many cases tensile strength was reduced. The gains were principally in softening point and stiffness, although weight for weight these gains were moderate compared with those obtained with short glass fibres (Table 1.8). The reason for the limited efficiency of particulate matter is not simple, and the theoretical prediction of composite properties is not easy. Numerous equations have been derived from the law of mixtures and are used to give a range of values to be expected. For example, Hashin and Strikeman derived

$$K_f + \cfrac{1-\phi_f}{\cfrac{1}{K_r-K_f}+\cfrac{3\phi_f}{3K_f+G_f}} \geqslant K_c \geqslant K_r + \cfrac{\phi_f}{\cfrac{1}{K_f-K_r}+\cfrac{3(1-\phi_f)}{3K_r+4G_r}} \qquad (1.3)$$

**Table 1.8** The effect of fillers on polypropylene.

| | Tensile strength (MPa) | Flexural modulus (GPa) | HDT (1.81 MPa) (°C) | Mould shrinkage (%) | Thermal expansion coefficient ($10^5 \times$ mm/mm °C) |
|---|---|---|---|---|---|
| Polypropylene | 38 | 1.5 | 35 | 1 −2.5 | 9 |
| 40% talc-filled PP | 33 | 3.8 | 100 | 0.8–1.5 | 6.5 |
| 40% chalk-filled PP | 24 | 2.8 | 70 | 0.7–1.4 | 3.4 |
| 30% glass-filled PP | 82 | 6.8 | 150 | 0.4 | 3 |

where $K$ is the bulk modulus of the filler ($f$), composite ($c$) and polymer matrix ($r$) and $\phi_f$ is the volume fraction of the filler. Such equations are of limited use in practice because many of their assumptions are invalid. The reinforcement depends, for example, upon the particle geometry, size and size distribution, particle porosity, the chemical nature of the particle surface and the dispersion of the filler in the polymer. Impurities in the filler may also have significant effects. Although the above factors play a role in all aspects of reinforcement, it is the strength properties, especially tensile strength, which are particularly susceptible.

The major problem is that a particle acts as a stress concentration point so that when a mechanical stress is applied to the composite, cracks can form in the system at much lower applied stress levels than in unfilled polymer. The stress concentration points are a short distance from the polymer–particle interface and the crack starts in the matrix. A crack will then propagate to a particle and, if adhesion between polymer and particle is poor, the crack can run around the particle with ease. The geometry of the particle is important because irregular shapes will lead to higher stress concentrations and therefore failure at lower applied stresses. The ideal particle shape from this point of view is a sphere.

Small particle sizes are preferred because they allow a greater surface area of contact with polymer. The problem with using small particle sizes (1–30 µm) is the handling of the powder in the compounding process. There is a tendency for particles to agglomerate resulting in poor dispersion. These agglomerates are not only potentially less able to resist crack propagation, but also are likely to be sources of crack initiation due to the loosely bound particle agglomerate splitting under applied stress. The porosity of the particles appears to play a role in that it allows 'keying' between polymer and particle.

### 1.4.3 Materials

The most commonly used fillers are calcium carbonate, talc, micas, silicas and clays.

*Calcium carbonate* ($CaCO_3$), known also as chalk or whiting, is obtained from impure (up to 5%) chalk deposits and is dry-ground to particle sizes down to 12 µm. It is also obtained from limestone which, by wet or dry grinding, can produce smaller particle sizes (less than 1 µm). High purity chalk can be obtained by chemical precipitation (precipitated chalk) which allows control of the particle size and shape. Precipitated chalk is also known as synthetic chalk. Chalk is still the most commonly used filler in thermoplastics, despite its limited reinforcing ability even when coupling agents are added. It is used with PVC and polypropylene to improve dimensional stability.

*Talc* is hydrous magnesium silicate ($Mg_2Si_4O_{10}(OH)_2$ and it occurs in many forms of which steatite is the purest. Purified ground particles have sizes in the range 1–50 µm and can form plate-like structures due to cleavage of the layered structure.

*Clays* are aluminium silicates, the most commonly used forms being china clay (kaolinite) and calcined clay. The latter ($Al_2Si_2O_7$) is made by heating china clay ($Al_2Si_2O_5(OH)_4$) at 600°C. Like talc, it forms plate-like structures with particle sizes in the range 0.3–20 µm, depending on the source and method of manufacture. Because the aspect ratio is greater than one (up to about 20), the plate-like particles of talc and calcined clay have better reinforcing properties than chalk. Reinforcement is improved by the use of coupling agents. Shrinkage, however, is greater than when chalk is used and some anisotropy occurs in mouldings.

Both talc and clays are used principally with PVC, polypropylene and nylons, but use with other polymers is increasing. Talc and calcined clay also improve electrical resistance properties. A synthetic sodium aluminium silicate is available which is used as a colour extender as well as a reinforcement.

Several other forms of aluminium silicate, including *micas*, are used increasingly in conjunction with coupling agents. Micas are complex aluminosilicates which include various other metal ions such as potassium (potash mica; muscovite; white mica, $K\,Al_2(Si_3Al)O_{10}(OH)_2$) and magnesium (magnesium mica; phlogphite, $K\,Mg_3(Si_3Al)O_{10}(OH)_2$). Micas have cleavage planes allowing production of plate-like particles which are potentially good reinforcing particles. A problem is that resins do not wet micas easily and reinforcement is poor unless coupling agents are used. Micas also have good electrical properties and mica filled plastics have excellent dielectric strength.

Further, micas are transparent to microwaves and are used in conjunction with polymers in moulding microwave wares.

*Wollastonite* is chiefly calcium metasilicate (CaSiO$_3$) with an aspect ratio of 20:1 and is available in grades which vary from fine powders to fibrous forms. The latter are those used for reinforcement and in addition they produce enhanced electrical insulation properties. There is considerable interest in wollastonite because its effect on melt viscosity is less than that of most other inorganic fillers. There is evidence, for example, that in some PVC formulations, the melt viscosity is less than in the unfilled polymer.

*Silica* (SiO$_2$) has many sources including quartz, sand and flint. High quality silica can be obtained by washing and grading as silica sand or, if pulverised, as silica flour. Precipitated silica—made by precipating silica from sodium silicate solutions with acids—is the form most commonly used with thermoplastics. Colloidal silica hydrogel has some uses, for example, as the reinforcement for acrylic materials in dentures.

It is worthwhile to note that many other fillers are used for specific, but non-reinforcing purposes. These include: alumina to improve hardness and wear resistance, antimony trioxide in conjunction with halogenated compounds as a fire retardant, barium ferrite to impart magnetic properties, barium sulphate to give X-ray opacity, molybdenum disulphide as a friction modifier to improve wear resistance (it also aids processing), titanium dioxide as a white pigment (the rutile form also has a reinforcing effect), zinc oxide which improves hardness and heat stability as well as acting as a white pigment and magnesium oxysulphate which is used to improve impact resistance in polypropylene.

*Alumina trihydrate* (ATH) is used mainly to produce fire retardant formulations. When heated to around 200°C, it decomposes endothermically liberating water. Unfortunately, its use with thermoplastics is limited to those with melt processing temperatures of 200°C or less, e.g. polypropylene. If loadings are sufficiently high (60%), polypropylene is rendered fire resistant and achieves a rating of V–0 on the Underwriters Laboratory UL94 test. Such high filler contents are only possible through the use of surface treatments to the ATH. Untreated, processing is impossible because flow is extremely difficult, probably because of poor dispersion, and localised heating produces temperatures in excess of 200°C which liberate steam.

## 1.5 Surface treatments

In the preceding sections numerous references have been made to coupling agents. As the name implies, these agents are used to couple the polymer and the fibre or mineral filler, thereby increasing adhesion. Coupling agents are essentially short chain hydrocarbon molecules, one end of which is compatible or inter-reactive with the polymer whilst the other end is capable of reacting with the fibre or filler. Usually, the fibre or powder is treated with the coupling agent before incorporation into the polymer and becomes coated with a chemically bound surface layer of the agent:

$$\boxed{\begin{array}{c}S\\U\\R\\F\\A\\C\\E\end{array}} + X—R \rightarrow \boxed{\begin{array}{c}S\\U\\R\\F\\A\\C\\E\end{array}}—R$$

Several types of coupling agent are in use, but there is no universal coupling agent suitable for all filler–polymer systems. Some are more generally applicable than others, whilst some are very specific. The reasons are that the different inorganic surfaces require variations in X to be able to react, and different polymers require variations in R to maximise compatibility and, in some cases, to permit specific interactions.

One of the most commonly used types of coupling agents are the *organosilanes* which may be represented by the general formula

$$R—Si—(OX)_3$$

where X is methyl, ethyl, methoxyethyl etc. and R is a suitable hydrocarbon chain. They have been used for many years with glass fibres in which case the —OX groups react with the —OH groups on the glass surface:

$$\begin{array}{ccc}
\phantom{Si}|\phantom{—OH} & & \phantom{Si}| \\
O & & O \\
| & & | \\
Si—OH + XO—R & \longrightarrow & Si—O—R + HOX \\
| & & | \\
O & & O \\
| & & |
\end{array}$$

Another major group of coupling agents are the *titanates* which were introduced in 1974. Of primary importance are the monoalkoxytitanates and the neoalkoxytitanates, the latter becoming available in 1984. The general formula of these titanates can be represented by

$$X—O—Ti \left[ O—\overset{\displaystyle O}{\overset{\|}{P}}—O—\overset{\displaystyle O}{\overset{\|}{P}}—(OR)_2 \right]_3$$
$$\hspace{2cm} \underset{OH}{|}$$

R is usually a short chain hydrocarbon such as $C_8H_{17}$ and X is a group capable of reacting with the filler or fibre. The advantage of the neoalkoxytitanates is their greater thermal stability which allows them to be added to the filled compound at the processing stage by direct feed to the hopper as masterbatch rather than having to treat the filler prior to incorporation into the polymer. The neoalkoxytitanates also have improved resistance to hydrolysis which allows coupling to be maintained at higher humidities and temperatures in service.

*Zircoaluminium* organometallic compounds are similar to the titanates and are used increasingly with a range of polymers and fillers. Polypropylene has benefited from the use of several specifically designed coupling agents such as fatty acids of castor oil and maleated polypropylene waxes.

As well as promoting adhesion, coupling agents also perform other functions which are particularly beneficial with mineral powders. There is the tendency for inorganic powders to adsorb (and absorb) moisture which causes agglomeration of particles within a film of moisture and with entrapment of air. This results in poor dispersion of the filler, poor reinforcement and poor processability which limits the amount of filler that can be incorporated into the polymer. Coupling agents act as hydrophobic wetting agents which displace the water and air to give a more stable and uniform dispersion of protected particles. Melt viscosity, which increases with filler content, is much lower when treated particles are used and this allows much higher filler loadings. For example, successful processing of polymers with up to 70% filler have been reported using titanate coupling agents. The authors are aware of one treatment (Alcan Chemicals S21) which permits the use of 60% ATH in polypropylene with only a small reduction in MFR from 17 to 16. The effect on processability is dependent on the polymer, filler and coupling agent.

Surface treatments other than coupling agents can aid dispersion and processability. These include wetting agents which are polarised molecules (anionic and cationic) with one end attracted to the filler or fibre and the other to the polymer. The wetting agent forms a protective layer around the filler/fibre thereby improving dispersion. It also promotes adhesion by allowing the polymer melt to wet the solid surface more efficiently. The essential difference between a wetting agent and a coupling agent is that the latter forms a chemical bond with the solid inclusion whereas the former does not. Classification is sometimes difficult.

Stearic acid and stearates have been used for many years to treat calcium carbonate and other fillers. The principal function of these materials appears to be to aid dispersion and hence ease processing. Their ability to improve reinforcement is minor.

## 1.6 Polymer blends

### 1.6.1 Introduction

Polymer blends are one of the most active areas of growth in polymer materials over the last ten years or so. A polymer blend is a physical mixture of two, or sometimes more, different polymers. The term is usually used to refer to mixtures in which the polymers are of different chemical types, say

PVC and nitrile rubber. Sometimes, however, the term refers merely to mixtures of polymers of the same type but different grades, e.g. of different molecular weight. Nominally, blends are simple physical mixtures, but in practice the blending process often gives rise to some covalent chemical bonding between the different types of polymer molecule, i.e. some grafting occurs. This grafting is often beneficial and is encouraged. Copolymers are not usually considered to be blends, although block copolymers have many of the characteristics of blends (see Chapter 3).

Polymer blends have long been used in the rubber industry. Their earliest significant use as plastics materials dates from the late 1940s when rubbers were blended with polystyrene in order to improve toughness, resulting in the well-known high impact polystyrene (HIPS) and, later, ABS materials. A similar rubber toughening of PVC was also developed at an early stage. For many years these two uses of blends remained the only large-scale uses of blends as plastics. It is only in the last ten years or so that blending has been carried out extensively with a wider range of polymers. Much of this growth of interest has concentrated on improvement of the mechanical performance of engineering plastics. Indeed, it has been predicted recently that by the mid-1990s half of all engineering plastics will be blends.

The importance of polymer blends as useful commercial materials centres on three areas:

(i) Rubber toughening of relatively brittle and stiff plastics—an extension of the earlier use of rubbers to toughen PS and PVC to many other polymers;

(ii) Blends of two relatively stiff plastics (often inappropriately called polymer alloys) in order to achieve a desirable balance of mechanical/ thermal performance and cost. Often this involves engineering plastics, as with ABS/polycarbonate and polyphenylene oxide/PS which are early classic examples of this type;

(iii) Blends as thermoplastic elastomers, which are discussed in Chapter 3.

### 1.6.2 The nature of polymer blends

The mixing of two chemical components is governed by the free energy change that occurs on mixing ($\Delta G_m$) according to:

$$\Delta G_m = \Delta H_m - T\Delta S_m \tag{1.4}$$

where $\Delta H_m$ and $\Delta S_m$ are the enthalpy and entropy of mixing respectively and $T$ is the temperature (in Kelvin). If $\Delta G_m$ is negative, mixing will occur spontaneously and a solution will be produced. In the case of mixing ordinary low molecular weight components, $\Delta S_m$ is highly positive (mixing is a randomising process) and hence, since $-T\Delta S_m$ will be negative, mixing is highly favoured. Usually $\Delta H_m$, which depends upon energetic interactions between the molecules, is also positive and thereby unfavourable for mixing.

However, the positive $\Delta H_m$ is often outweighed by the favourable entropy term so that mixing occurs, i.e. a solution of the two components is formed. The more similar the chemical nature of the two components (reflected in the similarity of their solubility parameters), the lower is the value of $\Delta H_m$ and the more likely mixing becomes. This is often expressed by the saying 'like dissolves like'.

In polymer–polymer mixtures, i.e. polymer blends, similar factors determine $\Delta H_m$ (here, the energetic interactions between the segments of the polymer chains) but $\Delta S_m$ is much less positive, randomisation being much more restricted because of the large size of the molecules involved. Although $-T\Delta S_m$ is still favourable, it is much less so and in most cases is unable to overcome the unfavourable $\Delta H_m$ term. Thus, most pairs of polymers are immiscible and are said to be incompatible. When mixed together they form a two-phase system rather than a single-phase solution, with one polymer dispersed as particles in a matrix of the other polymer. The $\Delta S_m$ term obviously is dependent on molecular size, and the miscibility of polymers decreases as molecular weight increases.

The conclusion of these fundamental thermodynamic considerations is that for the high molecular weight polymers used as plastics and rubbers, incompatibility and immiscibility are the rule, unless the two polymers are so closely similar in their chemical nature that $\Delta H_m$ is extremely small. In rare cases, $\Delta H_m$ may be negative if the two polymers show some strong specific interaction, such as hydrogen bonding, with each other, and miscibility may result. The classic example of a highly compatible and miscible polymer pair—and one of the few of commercial significance as a plastic—is polyphenylene oxide (PPO)/PS (General Electric's Noryl$^{TM}$). As with low molecular weight components, the likelihood of a pair of polymers being miscible can often be judged by the similarity of their solubility parameters. Complete miscibility is predicted to occur only if the value of the polymer/polymer interaction parameter $(\chi)$ is less than a critical value $(\chi)_{crit}$ given by

$$(\chi)_{crit} = 0.5[(1/m_1)^{0.5} + (1/m_2)^{0.5}]^2 \qquad (1.5)$$

and

$$\chi = V(\delta_1 - \delta_2)^2/RT$$

where $m_1$ and $m_2$ are the degrees of polymerisation, 1 and 2 are the solubility parameters of the two polymers respectively and $V$ is the molar volume of the smallest repeat unit, often taken as $10\,cm^3$.

The almost universal immiscibility of polymer pairs in blends (and hence their two-phase structure) does not necessarily mean that the blends have poor properties. On the contrary, the excellent toughening effects of small amounts of rubbers in plastics depend on the presence of dispersed rubber particles. However, if incompatibility is too great then interfacial adhesion between the dispersed polymer phase and the continuous matrix polymer will be poor and this does have a serious effect on the strength properties of the blend. It is the high incompatibility of many polymer pairs, resulting in blends of low strength (especially impact strength), that has until recently prevented blending from becoming more widely practised. This position has changed dramatically in recent years as chemists and technologists have found ways of 'compatibilising' otherwise incompatible polymers. The techniques developed have involved modifying one of the polymers by the incorporation of a compatibilising comonomer or by the use of a third polymer component as a compatibiliser. This latter is often a block copolymer consisting of blocks of each of the two component polymers to be compatibilised. The copolymer functions by aggregating at the interface in a manner similar to a surface active agent which stabilises an emulsion or suspension.

### 1.6.3 Factors influencing the properties of polymer blends

The properties of a polymer blend depend on several factors which are themselves interdependent. These include:

(i) choice of polymers;
(ii) composition;
(iii) compatibility of the polymers;
(iv) phase morphology;
(v) method of blend preparation.

Factors (i) and (ii) are obvious, but it is often the case that the properties of a blend do not depend in a simple manner on its composition. A property may reach some maximum or minimum value as composition varies. Such behaviour often can be correlated with a change in phase structure at the composition where the maximum or minimum value or other discontinuity occurs.

The most important change in phase morphology that can occur is phase inversion, when the blend structure changes from that of a matrix of polymer A containing dispersed phase polymer B to that of A dispersed in B. In general, it is the matrix phase polymer which is more important in determining the blend properties, even if it is present in the lower amount.

The theories and equations developed to describe the properties of composite materials often may be useful in predicting the properties of polymer blends, which can be considered to be a particular type of composite. Rubber-toughened plastics are sometimes described as *inverted* composites since they consist of a soft rubber phase dispersed in a harder plastic phase, in contrast to a classical composite where the dispersed phase is stiffer. In equations for these, the composition is often expressed as volume fractions.

The phase morphology, and hence blend properties, is often determined in practice by the method of blend preparation, which is normally melt mixing. The general aim is to achieve as fine a dispersion of the minor component as possible. This frequently means the use of high shear compounding equipment and long mixing times. Frequently, the dispersion consists of spherical particles of the minor component, though roughly shaped 'torn' particles may result when the dispersed phase has a very high viscosity. The lower melt viscosity component is more likely to form the continuous phase.

The compatibility of the polymer components is crucial in determining the blend properties, most importantly the strength properties. As explained above, it is the limited compatibility of most polymer pairs that has until recently restricted the commercial use of blends. At one extreme, if the polymers are so compatible that they are completely miscible, forming a single-phase blend, then the properties may be related to blend composition in a simple linear manner. A good example of this behaviour is the PPO/PS blends where a single blend $T_g$ is observed between the $T_g$ values of the PPO (210°C) and PS (100°C) separately, the value varying in proportion to the composition. Typical commercial PPO/PS blends have a $T_g$ of about 150°C. However this situation is rare, as explained above, and most polymer blends are two-phase systems, with two $T_g$ values, one characteristic of each separate component. The $T_g$ behaviour is often a useful measure of blend compatibility since as the polymers become more compatible, the component $T_g$'s broaden until, at complete miscibility, they merge to a single intermediate $T_g$. At the opposite extreme, when the two polymers are so completely incompatible that there is no interfacial adhesion between the two phases, no stress transfer to the dispersed phase is possible on stressing. The dispersed polymer particles therefore act as if they are holes and the blend has very poor strength properties as a consequence.

### 1.6.4 Rubber toughening of plastics

This is the longest established and still the most important commercial use of polymer blends. The early development of toughened polystyrene and PVC has already been mentioned. Today, more toughened PS (as HIPS and ABS) is sold than untoughened types. Furthermore, both HIPS and ABS are themselves often further blended with other polymers, as in PPO/HIPS and polycarbonate/ABS. Remarkable toughening effects can be achieved in both PS and PVC—up to about 100-fold increases in measured Izod impact strength are possible. In the case of PS, the rubber is polybutadiene for both HIPS and ABS and a special blend preparation technique is used in which the styrene monomer (plus acrylonitrile in the case of ABS) is polymerised in the presence of the rubber. This method produces a blend whose properties are enhanced by the grafting that occurs to the rubber and which has rubber particles which contain large polystyrene inclusions, thus increasing the effective rubber volume fraction.

In most other rubber-toughened plastics the blends are produced by melt mixing techniques. In the case of PVC many different impact modifiers are

**Table 1.9** Properties of styrene based polymers and PVC

| | | PS | HIPS | ABS | PVC | Toughened PVC |
|---|---|---|---|---|---|---|
| Izod impact strength | (J/12.7 mm) | 0.15–0.35 | 0.3–2.0 | 2.0–8.2 | 0.7–2.0 | 10 |
| Tensile strength | (MPa) | 35–85 | 20–50 | 18–60 | 160 | 40 |
| Elongation at break | (%) | 1.0–2.5 | 7–50 | 10–150 | 2–40 | — |
| Tensile modulus | (GPa) | 2.8–4.0 | 1.8–3.0 | 0.7–3.0 | 4.2 | 2.4 |
| HDT (0.45 MPa) | (°C) | 65–110 | 65–95 | 75–108 | 74 | 71 |

used including nitrile rubber, ethylene-vinyl acetate rubber, chlorinated polyethylene, ABS and acrylate rubbers. Unfortunately, blending with a rubber causes a loss of transparency due to the rubber particles' scattering light. This is often undesirable in PVC, but careful selection of a rubber with a similar refractive index to the polymer can give a clear blend. With PVC, methyl methacrylate–butadiene–styrene (MBS) is used for this purpose.

The incorporation of a rubber, not surprisingly, reduces the stiffness and softening point of a plastic, so rubber additions are restricted to about a 20% maximum. In general, 10–20% rubber is used. Some typical properties of toughened polystyrenes and PVC are shown in Table 1.9.

In recent years, rubbers with good compatibility with many other plastics, especially engineering plastics, have been developed. So called super-tough nylons and acetals are now quite well known. Again, extra toughness is achieved at the expense of loss in stiffness and reduction in softening temperature, as illustrated in Table 1.10.

Rubber toughening is particularly desirable when a filler (particulate or fibrous) is used to stiffen a polymer, but—as frequently happens—this also causes an unfortunate reduction in toughness. A good example is the combined use of glass fibre and rubber toughening agent in polypropylene, which sufficiently upgrades the mechanical performance of this polymer to that of a true engineering polymer class (Table 1.11)

A combination of stiffening *and* toughening fibre with a toughening rubber can give a truly superb reinforcement of both stiffness and toughness.

**Table 1.10** Properties of untoughened and super-tough (ST) dry Nylon 66 and Acetal

| | | Acetal | ST acetal | Nylon 66 | ST nylon 66 |
|---|---|---|---|---|---|
| Tensile strength | (MPa) | 69 | 45 | 83 | 52 |
| Elongation | (%) | 40 | 200 | 60 | 60 |
| Flexural modulus | (GPa) | 2.8 | 1.4 | 2.8 | 1.7 |
| Notched Izod | (J/m) | 75 | 907 | 53 | 112 |
| HDT (1.81 MPa) | (°C) | 136 | 90 | 90 | 83 |

**Table 1.11** Properties of reinforced polypropylenes

|  |  | PP | 30% Coupled GF PP | Rubber-toughened 30% Coupled GF PP |
|---|---|---|---|---|
| Tensile yield stress | (MPa) | 38 | 86 | 40 |
| Flexural modulus | (GPa) | 1.5 | 6.5 | 3.3 |
| Izod impact strength | (kJ/m$^2$) | 4.0 | 10.0 | 30 |
| HDT (1.81 MPa) | (°C) | 50 | 148 | 100 |

### 1.6.5  Blends of stiff plastics

This type of blend was developed later than the rubber-toughened plastics, but is similar in that only a few examples were initially of commercial significance. The two longest established materials are the PPO/PS type, already discussed, and polycarbonate (PC)/ABS blends. Today a much wider variety of this type of blend is produced than of any other kind. The growth in their number in the last few years has been quite remarkable. This has resulted from the development of new compatibilisation techniques to overcome the poor compatibility that normally exists between polymer pairs.

Most of these blends consist of mixtures of a cheaper, lower performance polymer with a more expensive but higher performance polymer. They may be viewed either as upgrading the performance of the cheaper polymer (at some increase in cost) or as lowering the cost of the higher performance polymer, but at some sacrifice in properties. The classic example of this latter type is PC/ABS produced by Bayer (Bayblend™), BASF (Terblend B™), Borg–Warner, now General Electric, (Cycoloy™) and Dow (Pulse™). Some typical properties are shown in Table 1.12. It can be seen from Table 1.12 that the ABS reduces the PC softening point, stiffness and 23°C impact strength, but lowers the cost. It is interesting that in some PC/ABS blends, a synergistic improvement in low-temperature impact strength may occur. Similar blends with acrylonitrile–styrene–acrylate rubber (ASA) replacing ABS (BASF Terblend S™) have improved UV light and heat resistance. These blends are widely used in automotive products such as fascias, arm rests and heater ducts and in machine housings, especially for business machines.

**Table 1.12** Properties of polycarbonate blends and component polymers

|  |  | PC | PBT | PC/PBT | PC/ABS |
|---|---|---|---|---|---|
| Tensile strength | (MPa) | 65 | 35 | 55 | 40 |
| Yield elongation | (%) | 1  –8 | 6 | 5 | 4  –  5 |
| Tensile modulus | (GPa) | 2.3 | 2.2 | 2.0 | 2.0 |
| Izod impact strength | (kJ/m$^2$) | 65 | 5 | 4 | 10  –  50 |
| HDT (1.82 MPa) | (°C) | 135 | 55 | 95 | 95  –105 |

**Table 1.13** Properties of PVC/SMA and PVC/ABS blends

|  |  | PVC | PVC/SMA 70/30 | PVC/ABS 70/30 |
|---|---|---|---|---|
| Tensile strength | (MPa) | 55 | 50 | 51 |
| Tensile modulus | (GPa) | 3.0 | 2.5 | 2.5 |
| Izod impact strength | (kJ/m²) | 35 | 165 | 188 |
| Vicat temperature | (°C) | 79 | 110 | 89 |

Another popular polycarbonate blend is that with polybutylene terephthalate (PBT) (Bayer's Makroblend™, BASF's Ultrablend™, General Electric's Xenoy™). This PC/PBT blend illustrates other benefits of blending. It combines the good environmental stress cracking, chemical and oil resistances and good melt flow of PBT with the toughness and heat resistance of PC. As with PC/ABS, there is also the added benefit of improved low-temperature impact resistance. Some properties of this blend are compared with the constituent polymers in Table 1.12. The blend is used mainly in automotive applications, especially for car bumpers (where it will withstand the paint oven stoving temperatures) and in electrical parts and housings.

Plastic–plastic blends are also of increasing importance in non-engineering polymers. An example which illustrates how the performance of a cheap polymer may be enhanced is the blend of PVC with styrene–maleic anhydride (SMA) (Monsanto's Cadon™). As shown in Table 1.13, the PVC softening point and impact strength are both improved.

A goal for many years in polymer blending has been to satisfactorily blend nylons (polyamides) with other engineering polymers. Such blends could take advantage of the high toughness, good stiffness, oil resistance and ease of processing of the nylon, whilst improving the heat resistance and water sensitivity of the nylon with the other polymer. To produce a satisfactory blend with nylons is difficult because of their polarity and hence lack of compatibility with most other polymers. Only recently has the necessary compatibilisation technology been developed and a spate of PA blends has reached the market in the last few years. In most cases these compatibility requirements are met by the use of a third special compatibilising polymer component. Important examples of this are the PPO (also called PPE)

**Table 1.14** Typical properties of nylon blends and component polymers

|  |  | PP | PA6 | PPE | PPE/PA | PP/PA6 |
|---|---|---|---|---|---|---|
| Tensile strength (Y) | (MPa) | 33 | 60 | 55 | 65 | 50 |
| Elongation | (%) | 600 | 300 | 35 | 70 | 300 |
| Tensile modulus | (GPa) | 1.2 | 2.5 | 2.7 | 2.3 | 1.8 |
| Izod impact strength | (kJ/m²) | 5.5 | 9 | 12 | 28 | 9 |
| HDT (0.45 MPa) | (°C) | 96 | 180 | — | — | 140 |
| Vicat temperature | (°C) | — | — | 135 | 206 | — |

blends with PA produced by General Electric (Noryl GTX™) and BASF (Ultranyl™). Some typical properties of a PPO/PA blend are shown in Table 1.14. The main use of these blends is again in automotive products such as body parts, radiator grills, spoilers and wheel covers and in business machine and electrical appliance housings.

Other examples of PA blends are PA/ABS (Monsanto's Triax™) which has an impact strength greater than that of the components—up to $100 \, kJ/m^2$—and PA/polypropylene (Atochem's Orgalloy™), some typical properties for which are shown in Table 1.14. PA/polyethylene blends are also possible by using a so-called *functionalised* modifier, in this case polyethylene containing acrylic acid, maleic acid or maleic anhydride (as in Exxon's Exxelar™), which will react with the PA, thus becoming grafted on. Such functionalised modifiers can also be used with PC, PBT and PET. In addition, ABS, MBS and all-acrylic modifiers which work in a similar manner are also available (Rohm and Haas's Paraloid EXL™) for use in PA, PBT and PC.

## 1.7 Conclusion

The use of additives such as fibres, particulate fillers or other polymers, often in combination, offers the possibility of tailoring a seemingly infinite variety of plastics materials to a very wide range of specified properties. Until relatively recently, the range of composite materials of practical use was somewhat limited because of incompatibility and dispersion problems leading to poor mechanical performance. In the last few years, developments in the production of long fibre reinforcements and compatibilisation techniques has been rapid so that now a very wide range of useful composite materials is commercially available and the range is likely to increase considerably in the future.

## Further reading

Alger, M. S. M. (1987) *Speciality Polymers* (ed. Dyson), Blackie, Glasgow, Chap. 3.
Birley, A. W., Heath, R. J. and Scott, M. J. (1988) *Plastics Materials* (2nd edn.), Blackie, Glasgow.
*British Plastics and Rubber*, March 1988.
Brydson, J. A. (1989) *Plastics Materials* (5th edn.), Iliffe.
Bucknall, C. B. (1977) *Toughened Plastics*, Applied Science.
Manson, J. A. and Sperling, L. H. (1975) *Polymer Blends and Composites*, Plenum Press.
Mascia, L. (1974) *The Role of Additives in Plastics*, Edward Arnold.
Monte, S. J. and Sugeman, G. (1985) *Developments in Plastics Technology-2* (ed. Whelan and Craft), Elsevier, London, Chap. 3.
Paul, D. R. and Barlow, J. W. (1980) *Rev. Macromol. Chem.* (C) **18**, 109.
Paul, D. R. and Newman, S. (1978) *Polymer Blends*, Academic Press, New York.
Seymour, R. B. (1985) *Developments in Plastics Technology-2* (ed. Whelan and Craft), Elsevier, London, Chap. 5.
Wake, W. C. (1977) *Fillers for Plastics*, Iliffe.
Whelan, A. and Goff, J. (1988) *Injection Moulding of Engineering Thermoplastics*, Whelan and Goff.

# 2 Performance of rubbers at high temperatures
K. S. LEE

## 2.1 Introduction

The exposure of a rubber product to elevated temperatures during its service life will result in gradual degradation of the product so that ultimately it may no longer fulfil its function. The rate at which this degradation takes place will be greatly accelerated under aerobic conditions, heat acting as a catalyst for the oxidation process. However, oxidation is confined to relatively thin articles or the outer layers of thick articles, as the diffusion of oxygen in rubber is a slow process, particularly in heavily oxidised layers [1].

In recent years service temperatures used have become higher and thus demands placed on rubber products to withstand heat ageing have increased. For example, in the automotive industry rubber components under the bonnet used to be required to withstand temperatures of 100°–110°C, but higher engine temperatures have led to demands for upgrading rubbers to meet 135°C, with the ultimate aim of 150°C.

The resistance of a product to heat ageing is seldom the only important factor. In the automotive applications mentioned, oil resistance, ozone resistance and physical properties such as low compression set will usually be required as well. Thus the technologist may have to reach a compromise in his selection of materials for meeting a high temperature specification in order to comply with other features of a specification.

## 2.2 Effects of ageing at high temperatures

The oxidative and anaerobic degradation of rubbers increase with time and temperature. The rate of oxidation of a natural rubber (NR) vulcanisate has been shown to double for every 7.5°C rise in temperature up to 90°C [1]. In high temperature environments structural changes in the vulcanisate occur with time. Scission of chains and cross-links may occur, accompanied by further cross-linking reactions which may or may not involve the vulcanising agent. If the scission reactions predominate, as is often the case in butyl and polyisoprene rubbers, then the modulus and hardness of the rubber decrease; if the cross-linking reactions are more prevalent, then the rubber stiffens with an increase in hardness and modulus together with a reduction in its elongation at break. The change in tensile strength of the rubber is not a good

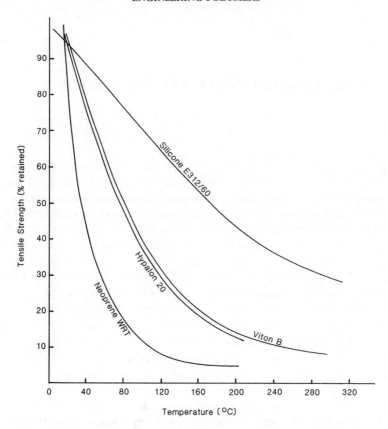

**Figure 2.1** Tensile strength as a function of temperature for various rubbers [15].

guide to the extent of degradation as it often increases in the early stages of ageing by continued cross-linking. However, eventually the vulcanisate strength will decrease, whatever the mode of heat degradation.

Other physical properties of the rubber are also affected by the temperature of the environment. An increase in temperature will lead to an immediate rise in vulcanisate resilience whilst the compression set will be adversely affected (partly due to changes occurring in the cross-linked network). The tensile strength of all rubbers decreases with increasing temperature, as shown in Figure 2.1. This illustrates the importance of carefully selecting the temperature at which a test is carried out. A rubber may be extremely resistant to the effects of ageing at a high temperature but be an unsuitable choice because of its loss of strength when its temperature is increased.

In addition, because they are hysteretic, rubbers increase in temperature when subjected to cyclic deformation. The environmental temperature may be low but a large cross-section lorry tyre, in which dissipation of heat is difficult, is likely to reach a running temperature of around 120°C. Prolonged service at such a temperature will lead to degradation of the rubber and possible failure of the tyre.

## 2.3  Nature of the rubber

Unlike many plastics, rubbers are not used on their own for the manufacture of a product. It is necessary to add a number of ingredients to ensure that the rubber compound is processable, the optimum vulcanisate properties are achieved and the product is competitive in price. These ingredients all affect the performance of the rubber vulcanisate at high temperatures; their influence will be discussed later. However, the inherent properties of the rubber itself are the major factor in deciding which particular material should form the basis of a compound.

### 2.3.1  Structural features

The heat resistance of a polymer is dependent on the dissociation energies of the various bonds present in its molecular structure, particularly those in the main chain. In rubbers, it is also strongly influenced by weak links such as double bonds in the main chain which are very responsive to oxidation [2]. Some typical bond dissociation energies are given in Table 2.1. Thus dienes such as natural rubber (NR) (cis-1,4-polyisoprene) and styrene–butadiene rubber (SBR) with their high levels of unsaturation are limited in their resistance to oxidative heat ageing; a ceiling of around 70°C is usually applied for continuous use. In contrast, the saturated fluorinated rubbers may be used continuously at 150°C and for periods of 24 h up to about 300°C. Again, it must be emphasised that the period of use at a particular temperature, or the ceiling temperature for a specified period, will increase considerably under anaerobic conditions.

**Table 2.1**  Typical dissociation energies for selected primary bonds

| Bond | Mean bond energy (kJ/mol) | Bond | Mean bond energy (kJ/mol) |
|------|---------------------------|------|---------------------------|
| O—O | 146 | Si—O | 368 |
| Si—Si | 178 | N—H | 389 |
| S—S | 270 | C—H | 430–510 |
| C—S | 272 | O—H | 464 |
| Si—C | 301 | C—F | 485 |
| C—N | 305 | C=C | 611 |
| C—Cl | 327 | C=O | ~740 |
| C—C | 346 | (aldehydes and ketones) | |
| C—O | 358 | C≡N | 890 |

*Source*: reproduced from Brydson, J. A. (1978) *Rubber Chemistry*. Applied Science Publishers, London.

### 2.3.2 Natural rubber

NR has a molecular structure which is 100% *cis*-1,4-polyisoprene.

$$\sim\!\!\sim\!\!\sim\!\!-CH_2-\underset{\underset{CH_3}{|}}{C}\!\!=\!\!CH-CH_2-(CH_2-\underset{\underset{CH_3}{|}}{C}\!\!=\!\!CH-CH_2-)_n-\!\!\sim\!\!\sim\!\!\sim$$

The carbon–carbon double bond in NR is extremely reactive due to the presence of the adjacent methyl group. Although it is detrimental to the heat resistance of NR, it has the considerable advantage of making the rubber highly responsive to accelerated sulphur vulcanisation. Sulphur systems are favoured by technologists as control of the vulcanisation parameters (viz. the scorch or induction period, rate of cross-linking and extent of vulcanisation) is more easily achieved than with other curing agents.

It is essential when compounding NR for maximum heat resistance to select the most appropriate curing system to yield thermally stable cross-links (section 2.4), and a powerful antioxidant (section 2.6). The wide use of NR as a general purpose rubber is based on its excellent physical properties which include high tensile strength, tear resistance, abrasion resistance and resilience coupled with low hysteresis. To these properties are added low price and ease of processing.

### 2.3.3 Styrene–butadiene rubber

Like NR, SBR is a general purpose rubber, extensively used in tyres, but limited in heat resistance. A copolymer still predominantly made by emulsion polymerisation, it has a random sequence of styrene and butadiene units, in a weight ratio of 23:77 and a unit ratio of 1:6

$$\sim\!\!\sim\!\!\sim\!\!-\underset{\underset{\bigcirc}{|}}{CH}-CH_2-\!\!\sim\!\!\sim\!\!\sim\!\!-CH_2-CH\!\!=\!\!CH-CH_2-\!\!\sim\!\!\sim\!\!\sim$$

Although the double bond in the butadiene unit is slightly less active than in isoprene, it still responds strongly to sulphur vulcanisation and attack by oxygen. Thus the temperature limits placed on the use of NR products apply similarly to products based on SBR, and the same compounding principles apply.

Two major differences between SBR and NR are their hysteretic nature and strength at elevated temperatures. SBR has the higher hysteresis and therefore shows greater heat build-up in cyclic deformation; it also shows a far greater loss of strength than NR at elevated temperatures. The latter is particularly important in processing operations such as de-moulding which may be carried out at temperatures of 150°–180°C and result in the tearing of SBR vulcanisates. A hot-water bottle, de-moulded at 150°–160°C by the insertion of forceps to stretch the neck by a factor of 5–6, must be based on NR rather than SBR. This lack of hot tear strength is common to many synthetic rubbers including fluoroelastomers which are otherwise extremely heat-resistant.

### 2.3.4 Acrylonitrile–butadiene rubber

$$\text{~~~} -CH_2-CH- \text{~~~} -CH_2-CH=CH-CH_2- \text{~~~}$$
$$\quad\quad\quad | $$
$$\quad\quad\quad C\equiv N$$

Acrylonitrile–butadiene rubbers (NBR) are copolymers of acrylonitrile and butadiene in random sequence with the acrylonitrile content varying from 15% to 50%. They are polar in nature and used almost solely in applications where resistance to swelling by petroleum oils is required. Thus, specifications are required for oil resistance in addition to heat resistance.

Again, the double bonds in the butadiene units make the rubbers responsive to sulphur vulcanisation but limit the oxidative heat resistance of NBR-based products. If the product is *completely* immersed in oil at high temperature, then oxygen is absent and the effects on the rubber are less harmful than on a product in air at the same temperature. For a component exposed to both air and oil a maximum service temperature of 100°–110°C is applicable for continuous use. However, under conditions of complete immersion in oil a product is likely to withstand up to 160°C for long periods.

In recent years, the automotive applications of NBR have become more demanding as engine temperatures have risen. Although extensive compounding studies have yielded the optimum selection of vulcanising system, filler and antioxidant, the demand for resistance to 135°–150°C under oxidative ageing conditions is rather beyond the capabilities of an NBR vulcanisate.

A recent approach to the problem has been the manufacture of hydrogenated NBR, thus removing the reactive site in the butadiene units.

$$\text{~~~} -CH_2-CH- \text{~~~} -CH_2-CH=CH-CH_2- \text{~~~}$$
$$\quad\quad\quad | $$
$$\quad\quad\quad C\equiv N$$

$$\xrightarrow{[H_2]} \text{~~~} -CH_2-CH- \text{~~~} -CH_2-CH_2-CH_2-CH_2- \text{~~~}$$
$$\quad\quad\quad\quad\quad | $$
$$\quad\quad\quad\quad\quad C\equiv N$$

Complete hydrogenation yields a fully saturated rubber with improved oxidation resistance but also prevents sulphur vulcanisation and an organic peroxide would have to be used for cross-linking. However, if hydrogenation is not taken to completion, the small number (a few %) of reactive double bond sites remaining is sufficient for a sulphur system to be used. A commercial example of hydrogenated acrylonitrile–butadiene rubber (HNBR)

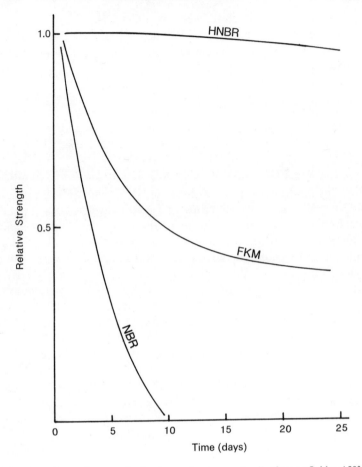

**Figure 2.2** Change in tensile strength after immersion in a crude oil reference fluid at 150°C in the presence of $H_2S$ [16].

is Therban™; Figures 2.2 and 2.3 illustrate the changes in tensile strength and elongation at break which occur when this rubber is immersed in a crude reference oil at 150°C in the presence of $H_2S$. The changes occurring in a conventional NBR and a fluoroelastomer (FKM) are also shown for comparison.

### 2.3.5 Polychloroprene rubbers

The polychloroprenes (CR) are polymers of 2-chloro-1,3-butadiene, being substantially (usually >80%) *trans*-1,4 configuration. The remainder of the structure is mainly *cis*-1,4 but small amounts of 1,2 (e.g. 1.5%) and 3,4 (e.g. 1%) configurations may be present. Although the polymer is unsaturated, the

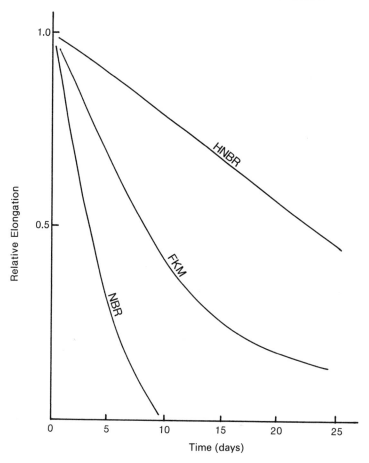

**Figure 2.3** Change in elongation at break after immersion in crude oil reference fluid at 150°C in the presence of H₂S [17].

effect of the chlorine atom is to de-activate the double bond so that the rubber behaves as though saturated. The polymer therefore has good oxidation and ozone resistance but vulcanisation has to take place via the use of metallic oxides. The presence of chlorine renders the polymer polar, making it resistant to some degree to swelling by petroleum oils and also conferring flame resistance. The combination of these properties with high strength leads to a rubber with an excellent balance of properties, although these are off-set to some extent by its price which is considerably higher than that of other dienes.

When maximum heat resistance is required, the type of CR used should be a mercaptan-modified polymer and the curing system of MgO 4.0 parts/hundred parts of rubber (phr)/ZnO 5.0 phr should be adjusted to MgO

4.0 phr/ZnO 10.0 phr plus a thiourea accelerator [3]. An oxtylated diphenylamine is the preferred antioxidant, at a level up to 6 phr, since this has a low level of volatility.

The maximum temperature at which CR vulcanisates can be used continuously is 90°–100°C, i.e. 20°–30°C higher than NR or SBR.

### 2.3.6 Ethylene–propylene rubbers

Ethylene–propylene rubbers (EP(D)M) result from copolymerisation of ethylene and propylene leading to a fully saturated polymer.

$$\text{\textasciitilde\textasciitilde\textasciitilde—CH}_2\text{—CH}_2\text{—\textasciitilde\textasciitilde\textasciitilde—CH}_2\text{—}\underset{\overset{|}{\text{CH}_3}}{\text{CH}}\text{—\textasciitilde\textasciitilde}$$

Useful commercial rubber grades are random in monomer sequence and contain 60–70% ethylene. In accordance with previous observations, the rubbers show excellent oxidation and ozone resistance compared with NR and SBR and this, combined with a relatively low price, has led to extensive use of EP(D)M in automotive and window sealing strips. Although it is not used for tyres it has gained acceptance at the expense of other oxidation and ozone resistant rubbers such as Butyl rubber so that its consumption now approaches the 1 million tonnes/annum mark.

For continuous use at temperatures around 120°C or intermittent periods around 150°C, the copolymer, cured by an organic peroxide and with a suitable high molecular weight antioxidant, is normally used. However, for less stringent applications, sulphur vulcanised terpolymers (EPDM), which contain a small percentage of a non-conjugated diene, are used. The diene is copolymerised to provide unsaturated sites but these sites are pendant to the main chain and do not have such a damaging effect as double bonds in the main chain. Examples of dienes used are ethylidene norbornene and 1,4-hexadiene.

A problem associated with the use of peroxides to vulcanise the copolymers (EPM) is that cross-linking is accompanied by chain scission. The network formed is therefore less than ideal in that the molecular weight of the rubber is being effectively reduced although the shorter chains are being cross-linked. The physical properties of the vulcanisate are therefore adversely affected. Although the terpolymers (EPDM) were produced to enable sulphur vulcanisation to take place, EPDM may be cured by a peroxide and less scission takes place than in EPM. Consequently, EPDM vulcanised by a peroxide may be used for high temperature resistance, particularly when a low level of compression set is also required.

### 2.3.7 Silicone rubbers

Silicone rubbers are semi-inorganic polymers of predominantly dimethyl siloxane (MQ)

$$\sim\!\!\sim\!\!\sim\!\!-O-\underset{\underset{\displaystyle CH_3}{|}}{\overset{\overset{\displaystyle CH_3}{|}}{Si}}-\left(O-\underset{\underset{\displaystyle CH_3}{|}}{\overset{\overset{\displaystyle CH_3}{|}}{Si}}-\right)_n\!\!-\!\!\sim\!\!\sim\!\!\sim$$

Modifications may be made by substituting small quantities of other groups (e.g. vinyl, phenyl) for methyl groups along the polymer chain.

The silicones possess outstanding properties; they are suitable for a temperature range from $-100°C$ to $+300°C$, have excellent oxidation and ozone resistance, chemical inertness, high electrical resistivity and physiological inertness. They are, however, expensive materials and their strength at room temperature is only moderate. The latter disadvantage is offset by their ability to retain a high proportion of their strength when the temperature is raised to, say, $150°C$.

Vulcanisation is by organic peroxides yielding stable C—C bonds in the cross-links. The vinyl modified poly(dimethyl siloxanes) (VMQ) respond better than the unmodified polymer to vulcanisation by the popular dicumyl peroxide.

The excellent heat resistance of silicone rubber is shown by the data in Table 2.2. It is of a considerably higher order than that of rubbers discussed previously. When silicone elastomers are heated above $200°C$ in close confinement, softening of the rubber and a loss of elastomeric properties may occur due to polymer reversion [4]. Correct compounding procedures reduce this effect to a low level.

Silicone rubbers are widely used for electrical insulation. A further feature of their use at very high temperatures is the retention of excellent dielectric properties.

## 2.3.8 Fluoroelastomers

Fluorinated rubbers show exceptional resistance to oxidation, ozone attack, chemicals and certain solvents. Their stability has been attributed to the high strength of the C—F bond compared with the C—H bond, to steric hindrance and to strong Van der Waal's force [5]. Their heat resistance is

**Table 2.2** Continuous operating temperature versus useful life

| Temperature (°C) | Service life (h) |
| --- | --- |
| 150 | 15 000–30 000 |
| 200 | 7500–10 000 |
| 260 | 2000 |
| 316 | 100 |
| 370 | 1 |

*Source*: reproduced from Lee, K. S. and Whelan, A. (1981) *Developments in Rubber Technology*, Vol. 2, Applied Science Publishers, London.

comparable to that of the silicone rubbers and like the silicones they are very expensive; on a volume basis, their cost is considerably increased by their high density (1.84).

Fluoro elastomers (FKMs) are all copolymers; examples are vinylidene fluoride–hexafluoropropylene and vinylidene fluoride–chlorotrifluoroethylene. Many different grades are available, often involving a third or even fourth monomer and sometimes an added curing agent. Various vulcanisation systems may be used including diamines, peroxides and bisphenol. The bisphenol system has led to marked improvements in compression set and stress-relaxation resistance at very high temperatures. Values of compression set as low as 15% have been recorded in a test conducted for 70 h at 200°C in

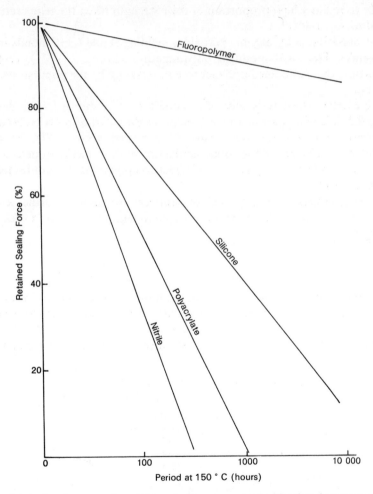

**Figure 2.4** Sealing force retention of fluoroelastomer compared with other elastomers used for seals [18].

air. Figure 2.4 shows the outstanding ability of FKM O-rings to retain their
sealing force at 150°C.

## 2.4 Vulcanising systems

### 2.4.1 Introduction

Vulcanisation is the insertion of chemical cross-links between long-chain
rubber molecules to form a network. The type of system used determines the
number and type of cross-links which are inserted. In turn, the type of
cross-link has a profound effect on the high temperature ageing characteristics
of the vulcanisate.

A full appraisal of all the vulcanising systems used in natural and synthetic
rubbers is beyond the scope of this work, but it must be borne in mind that
there is an optimum system for heat resistance in each rubber. The most
marked effects of cross-link type are in those rubbers that inherently show
poor resistance to thermal ageing, viz. polydienes, and also those in which a
small amount of diene is added to allow sulphur vulcanisation (e.g. EPDM).
Extensive studies have been made of vulcanising systems for these rubbers,
in particular by the Malaysian Rubber Producers Research Association
(MRPRA).

### 2.4.2 Organic peroxides

Vulcanisation by peroxides is a free radical process that leads to the
formation of carbon–carbon cross-linked networks.

$$POOP \xrightarrow{\Delta H} 2PO^{\bullet}$$
$$\text{peroxide} \qquad \text{oxy radicals}$$

$$PO^{\bullet} + RH \longrightarrow POH + R^{\bullet}$$
$$\qquad \text{rubber} \qquad\qquad \text{rubber radical}$$

$$2R^{\bullet} \longrightarrow R\text{—}R$$
$$\qquad\qquad \text{cross-linked rubber}$$

The carbon–carbon bond has a high dissociation energy and hence good
thermal stability. Technologically, however, the use of organic peroxides has
many undesirable features such as the lack of an induction period (leading to
scorch problems), odour, and lack of control over the rate of vulcanisation as
there are no accelerators of peroxide vulcanisation. In addition, there are
many reactions which compete with those shown above and create further
problems, viz. the presence of pendant vinyl groups in the polymer (as in SBR
and NBR) leads to excessive, uncontrolled cross-linking; antioxidants react
with the oxy radicals, reducing the cross-link density of the vulcanisate; in the
presence of oxygen, scission of some rubbers occurs during vulcanisation.
The strength of vulcanisates also tends to be low.

Despite these technological disadvantages organic peroxides are used
where sulphur cures are impossible due to the lack of unsaturation in the

rubber (ethylene–propylene rubber (EPR), silicones) and even in dienes when maximum heat resistance is required. Peroxide-cured NBR is an example of the latter, although the difficulty of selecting an antioxidant in conjunction with the peroxide imposes a restriction on the level of thermal oxidative resistance that can be attained.

### 2.4.3 Sulphur systems

In addition to the sulphur vulcanising agent, these systems contain an activator (e.g. zinc oxide plus stearic acid) and an organic accelerator. The mechanism of vulcanisation is complex and the nature of the cross-linked network produced varies according to the sulphur/accelerator ratio, vulcanisation time and temperature.

Figure 2.5 depicts the chemical structures that may be present in a vulcanised natural rubber network. The sulphur containing cross-links may be monosulphidic, disulphidic or polysulphidic ($S_x$) in which the value of $x$ is usually $<6$. Monosulphidic cross-links show greater thermal stability than polysulphidic types since the C—S bond has a higher dissociation energy than the S—S bond. In addition the main-chain modifications (f–h) contribute to poor oxidative ageing resistance of NR, as do the conjugated dienes and trienes. Thus a NR vulcanisate containing predominantly monosulphidic cross-links with little or no main-chain modification exhibits the best heat resistance that can be obtained when vulcanising by a sulphur or sulphur-donor system.

By contrast, networks of polysulphidic cross-links, with the attendant main-chain modification, give vulcanisates with better strength and fatigue

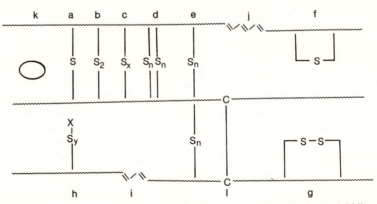

**Figure 2.5** Network structure [18]: (a) monosulphidic cross-link C–S–C; (b) disulphidic cross-link C—S—S—C; (c) polysulphidic cross-link C—$S_x$—C ($x$ = 3–6); (d) parallel vicinal cross-links C—$S_n$—C ($n$ = 1–6); (e) cross-links attached to common or adjacent carbon atoms; (f) intra-chain cyclic monosulphide; (g) intra-chain cyclic disulphide; (h) pendant sulphidic group terminated with accelerator fragment (X); (i) conjugated diene; (j) conjugated triene; (k) extra-network material; (l) carbon–carbon cross-link (probably absent).

**Table 2.3** Properties of NR cured with conventional and EV sulphur systems*

|  | Conventional | EV |
|---|---|---|
| Hardness (IRHD) | 67 | 67 |
| Resilience (%) at 21°C | 66 | 62 |
| Tensile strength (MPa) | 26.5 | 25.5 |
| Aged 14 days, 100°C | 6.1 | 17.3 |
| Elongation at break (%) | 490 | 495 |
| Aged 14 days, 100°C | 44 | 335 |
| Stress at 300% elongation (MPa) | 14.6 | 13.1 |
| Aged 14 days, 100°C | — | 14.7 |
| Fatigue life (0–100% strain, kc) | 44 | 34 |
| Aged 7 days, 100°C | <0.1 | 33 |
| Compression set (%) | 31 | 17 |

* Conventional compounds: NR 100; Dutrex R 5; HAF black 50; ZnO 5; lauric acid 1; sulphur 2.5; CBS 0.4; Flectol H 2. EV compounds: NR 100; Dutrex R 5; HAF black 50; ZnO 5, lauric acid 3; sulphur 0.25; CBS 1.8; TMTD 1.2; Flectol H 2.

*Source*: reproduced from *Compounding NR for heat resistance*, MRPRA Technical Bulletin, Malaysia.

properties. These are produced using a conventional sulphur system as follows: sulphur 2.5 phr; zinc oxide 5.0 phr; stearic acid 1.0 phr; *N*-cyclo-hexylbenzthiazyl sulphenamide (CBS) 1.0 phr.

The monosulphidic cross-linked network is given by the so-called efficient vulcanisation (EV) system, employing a low level of sulphur, with corresponding higher level of accelerator. An example of an EV system is: sulphur 0.5 phr; zinc oxide 5.0 phr; stearic acid 1.0 phr; CBS 5.0 phr.

It should be noted that these two systems, using the quantities of additives as suggested, give the same number of cross-links and hence approximately the same vulcanisate modulus. A compromise of the properties and costs of the conventional and EV systems may be obtained by adopting a semi-EV system.

The physical properties of NR vulcanisates cured with typical conventional and EV systems, unaged and aged at 100°C, are shown in Table 2.3. Ageing at 100°C represents severe conditions for a NR vulcanisate but the material cured with the EV system retains a high level of properties after 14 days. In particular, its elongation at break, a property which is very sensitive to network changes, remains as high as 335%. In contrast, the conventionally cured rubber is severely degraded and retains only about 10% of its original elongation at break.

### 2.4.4 Urethane systems

Urethane systems for the vulcanisation of NR and other diene rubbers are a more recent development in the search for thermally stable vulcanisates. Developed at MRPRA, they are based on the reaction products of nitroso-phenols with di-isocyanates and produce cross-links mainly of a urea type

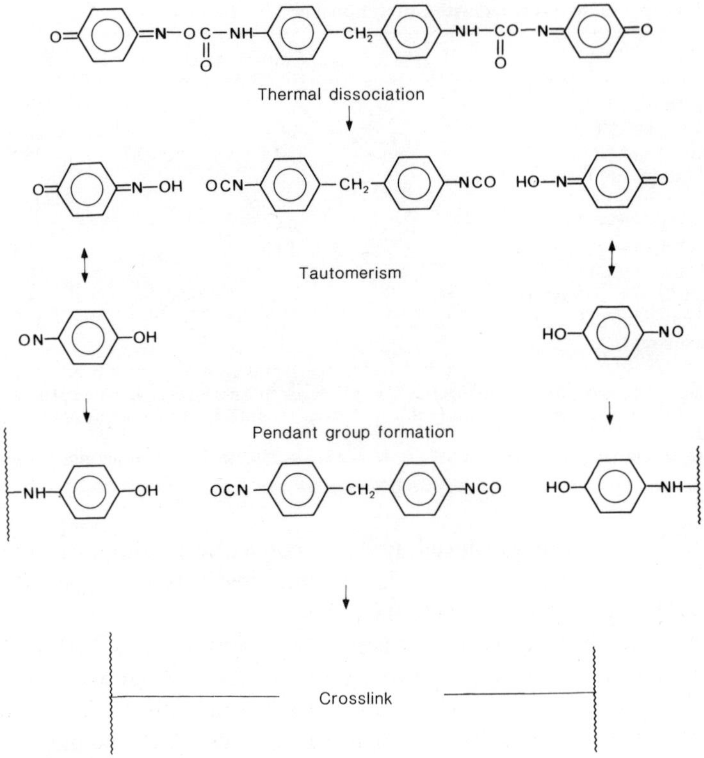

**Figure 2.6** Mechanism of urethane cross-liking [19].

(Figure 2.6). Vulcanisates obtained using urethane systems have a good balance of physical properties with emphasis on excellent resistance to reversion and oxidative heat ageing.

Used on their own, urethane systems give a slow rate of cure and are expensive. They may be mixed with sulphur systems to overcome these drawbacks and yield vulcanisates with high modulus and little loss of heat resistance compared with 100% urethanes. An adduct of nitrosophenol and di-isocyanate which dissociates at the vulcanisation temperature is used commercially.

Urethane or urethane/sulphur systems may be used in diene rubbers for the following reasons:

(a) where maximum reversion resistance is required when curing at very high temperatures (e.g. continuous vulcanisation of extrudates);
(b) to achieve a uniform cure throughout a thick article; and
(c) when outstanding fatigue resistance in a heat-aged product is required.

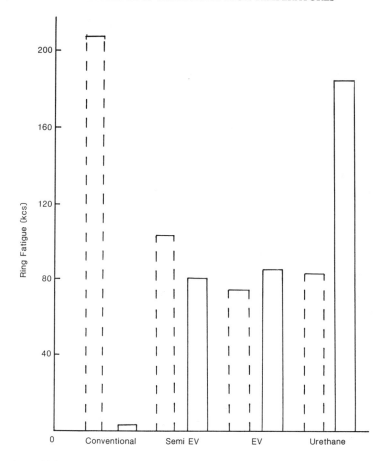

**Figure 2.7** Initial and aged fatigue performance [20]: -----, unaged; ————, aged at 100°C, 7 days.

Figure 2.7 illustrates the outstanding fatigue resistance *after* heat ageing of a NR vulcanisate, cured with a urethane.

## 2.5 Antioxidants

### 2.5.1 Introduction

The resistance of a rubber product to oxidative ageing may be considerably enhanced by the use of a chemical protective agent referred to as an antioxidant. Antioxidants are not used in silicones or fluoroelastomers but the less oxidation-resistant types of rubber all benefit from the addition of a small amount (usually 1–2 phr) of such an ingredient.

## 2.5.2 Oxidation reaction

The oxidative process is a free radical chain reaction.

*Initiation*:

$$RH + O_2 \rightarrow R^{\cdot}(+HO_2^{\cdot})$$
$$RH \quad\quad \rightarrow R^{\cdot}(+H^{\cdot}) \quad (RH = \text{rubber})$$

*Propagation*:

$$R^{\cdot} + O_2 \rightarrow RO_2^{\cdot}$$
$$RO_2^{\cdot} + RH \rightarrow ROOH + R^{\cdot}$$

*Termination*:

$$2R^{\cdot} \rightarrow R\text{—}R, \quad \text{a cross-link}$$

Chain scission reactions may also occur.

Antioxidants may be peroxide decomposers, causing ROOH to form non-radical products, or chain-interrupters. The most widely used anti-oxidants are the latter class, which react in the propagation stage.

$$AR + RO_2^{\cdot} \longrightarrow ROOH + A^{\cdot} \quad ((AH = \text{antioxidant})$$

Then

$$2A^{\cdot} \longrightarrow \text{inert product}$$

The commercially available antioxidants are phenol or amine derivatives. Whilst the latter are generally more powerful they have the disadvantages of discolouring light-coloured products and staining adjacent surfaces by migration.

In the consideration of an antioxidant to protect against thermal oxidation of a rubber, it must first be recognised that the stability of the rubber chain and the cross-links inserted dominate the rate of degradation. The improvement brought about by the antioxidant is of a lower order. Thus an NR compound cured with a conventional sulphur system and containing an antioxidant would not age as well at high temperatures as an EV-cured compound without antioxidant. Antioxidants, of course, also lead to improvements in resistance to other forms of ageing such as flex-cracking.

## 2.5.3 Selection of antioxidants

The selection of an antioxidant to enhance vulcanisate resistance to heat ageing must take into account the volatility of the antioxidant and its rate of diffusion in the rubber. Protection against oxidation is needed in the outer layers of a thick section and antioxidants have the ability to migrate from the interior to replenish used antioxidant in the outer layers as oxidation progresses, i.e. to act as a buffer. However, at high service temperatures the antioxidant may be volatilised and hence it is the practice in high temperature applications to use an antioxidant of high molecular weight and consequent low volatility; this type may have a slow rate of diffusion in the rubber. A widely used example of such an antioxidant is polymerised 2,2,4-trimethyl-1,2-dihydroquinoline; a level of 1–2 phr is usually incorporated as this is the optimum concentration.

In polychloroprene (CR), which is always vulcanised using metallic oxides, a dramatic improvement in heat resistance is obtained by using octylated diphenylamine. Here the improvement continues with increasing concentration of the antioxidant up to a level of 6 phr (Figure 2.8).

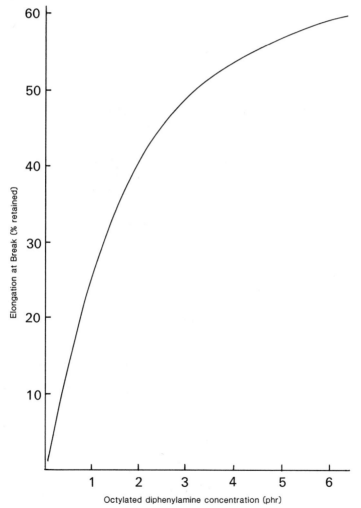

**Figure 2.8** Effect of octylated diphenylamine concentration on ageing of polychloroprene at 120°C for 8 days [21].

Synergism may be found in combinations of antioxidants, an outstanding example being the use of 2-mercaptobenzimidazole (MBI) in conjunction with a phenol or amine. The 4- and 5-methyl derivatives of MBI may also be used. Usually MBI, which has little effect on its own, and the second antioxidant are used in equal proportions by weight. However, in peroxide-cured EPM, the best results are obtained using a 4:1 ratio of MBI to amine [6].

Mention has already been made (section 2.4.2) of the reaction of anti-oxidants with oxy radicals in vulcanisation by organic peroxides. The effect of this reaction is to lower the level of cross-linking in the rubber with consequent reduction in modulus and other physical properties. The p-phenylene diamines, which have both antioxidant and antiozonant power, are notorious in this respect.

### 2.5.4 Bound antioxidants

Loss of antioxidant from the rubber product may occur by volatilisation or as a result of leaching when the product is immersed in a liquid. Oil-seals, hose linings, latex thread in clothes are examples of rubber articles that may have their antioxidant extracted.

The use of high molecular weight antioxidants to counteract volatilisation has already been mentioned. Both volatilisation and extraction may be prevented by anchoring the antioxidant to the rubber molecule forming the so-called rubber-bound antioxidant.

MRPRA have shown that N,N'-disubstituted quinone diimines (Figure 2.9)

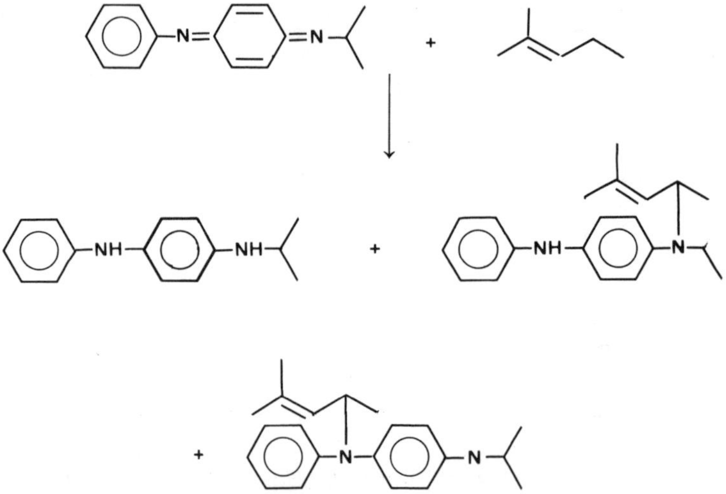

**Figure 2.9** Formation of a bound antioxidant.

and *N*-substituted quinone imines can react with rubber to give a *p*-phenylene diamine or *p*-aminophenol together with an antioxidant bound to the rubber. Scott [8] (Aston University) has also described the formation of bound antioxidants using sulphur-bearing phenols.

The only commercial application of this principle to date has been the production of NBR with a bound antioxidant formed during the polymerisation process. This method is based on the work of Kline and Miller [9] and Meyer *et al.* [10] and involves the use of *N*-(4-anilinophenyl)methacrylamide

## 2.6 Fillers

The choice of quantity and type of filler to be used in a rubber compound is governed mainly by the physical properties required in the finished product. Other factors such as the processing of the compound and the price of the product must also be considered. The use of silica is restricted as it is expensive and carbon black generally gives superior vulcanisate properties. Silica is normally used only in high quality articles in which a black colour is unacceptable. There is evidence, however, that the use of silica leads to superior heat resistance in the rubber vulcanisate. Where silica cannot be used as the sole filler because the vulcanisate properties are unacceptable, or the price is too high, then replacement of part of the carbon black content by silica (minimum 15 phr) will still lead to enhanced heat ageing resistance [11]. Table 2.4 gives data for the effects of silica in an epichlorhydrin vulcanisate.

An improvement in heat resistance brought about by the use of silica has also been found in NR, SBR, NBR and CR. Fine particle size calcium

**Table 2.4** Heat-resistant epichlorhydrin rubber*

| Hours ageing at 149°C | Tensile strength (% retained) | Elongation at break (% retained) |
|---|---|---|
| **HAF black** (N330) | | |
| 70 | 105 | 40 |
| 168 | 93 | 37 |
| 336 | 62 | 27 |
| **Silica** (Hi-Sil 233) | | |
| 70 | 99 | 60 |
| 168 | 88 | 50 |
| 336 | 75 | 40 |

*Compounds: ECO 100; dibasic lead phosphate 7; dibasic lead phthalate 10; internal lubricant 1; antioxidant 1, filler 50; thiourea 1 (0.5 with silica); mercaptosilane (silica only) 1.

*Source*: M. Q. Fetterman (1973) *Rubber Chem. Technol.*, **46**, 927.

carbonate has been found to give good heat resistance in polychloroprene vulcanisates but also leads to poor weathering and low physical properties.

## 2.7 Plasticisers

Plasticisers are used to improve the processing characteristics of a rubber compound by lowering its viscosity and assisting flow. They also lower the modulus and hardness of the vulcanised rubber and are therefore used in conjunction with the filler to control these properties. The use of plasticisers reduces the cost of raw materials of a product as they are cheaper than rubber and allow the use of increased filler loadings. The level of plasticiser which may be incorporated is limited by the level of rubber/plasticiser compatibility and the reduction in vulcanisate strength which occurs.

The main plasticisers used in the rubber industry are petroleum oils, although their use is largely restricted to non-polar rubbers. They are high-boiling petroleum fractions obtained after petrol and heating-oil fractions have been removed by distillation. Three principal types, all of wide molecular weight distribution, are used, viz. aromatic, naphthenic and paraffinic oils. Compatibility of an oil/rubber mixture is influenced by the proximity of their solubility parameters. Thus a paraffinic oil $(\delta = 15.3 \, \text{MJ/m}^3)^{\frac{1}{2}}$ is compatible with NR $(\delta = 16.5 \, \text{MJ/m}^3)^{\frac{1}{2}}$ but incompatible with CR $(\delta = 19.0 \, \text{MJ/m}^3)^{\frac{1}{2}}$.

When selecting an oil for use in a rubber for a high temperature application, the oxidation resistance of the oil and its volatility must be considered. The oxidative instability of an oil is due primarily to the presence of nitrogen and sulphur heterocyclics [12]; these heterocyclics tend to be concentrated in the aromatic portion of the oil. Thus aromatic oils tend to have the worst oxidative heat stability.

The volatility of the oil decreases as its molecular weight and viscosity increase. For a given molecular weight, aromatic oils tend to be more volatile than paraffinic oils, with naphthenics occupying an intermediate position. Diene and olefinic rubbers for use at high temperatures are, therefore, compounded with high molecular weight, high viscosity paraffinic oils.

High molecular weight, low volatility plasticisers are also obtained by the polymerisation of esters, e.g. polypropylene adipate. These materials are extremely viscous, present handling problems, do not plasticise well and are expensive. Their use is consequently very limited.

Liquid low molecular weight rubbers (e.g. liquid NBR) may be blended with rubber of normal molecular weight to act as a non-extractable, non-volatile plasticiser since the liquid polymer becomes cross-linked to the main rubber during vulcanisation. These plasticisers have the same drawbacks as the polymerised esters.

Where the maximum heat resistance is required an obvious ploy is to omit the plasticiser whenever possible.

## 2.8 Design of the rubber product

### 2.8.1 Degradation

The rate of degradation of a rubber product and hence the length of its service life is dependent on many factors including time and temperature, the thickness of the rubber article and the availability of oxygen [13].

It was stated earlier that anaerobic ageing is slow compared with thermal oxidative ageing and usually concerns changes only in the cross-link structure. Oxidative ageing extends to reactions involving the polymer chains. When the outer layers of a rubber product have been oxidatively degraded the rate of diffusion of oxygen through the oxidised layers is slow compared with its rate through unoxidised rubber. This factor, combined with the rapid

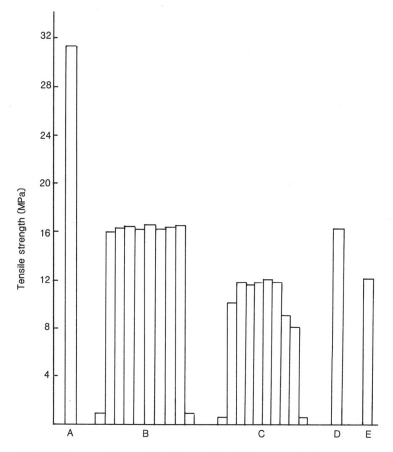

**Figure 2.10** Tensile strength retention of conventional NR gum vulcanisate, protected with IPPD, aged at 150°C (1): A, unaged sample 2.5 mm thick; B, simulated block made up of 2.5 mm sheets, aged in air for 2 days; C, simulated block, aged in air for 7 days; D, single sheet, 2.5 mm thick, aged *in vacuo* for 2 days; E, single sheet, aged *in vacuo* for 7 days.

consumption of oxygen, means that the inner bulk of a thick article is never oxidised but degrades only slowly through anaerobic thermal ageing.

Knight and Lim [1] carried out an experiment in which a large NR component was obtained by clamping together a number of thin rubber sheets. This component was aged in air at 150°C and then the sheets were separated and tested separately. The results showed that the two outer sheets (2.5 mm thick) suffered oxidative attack but the inner sheets behaved as if *in vacuo*. Figure 2.10 illustrates the results.

Therefore, rubber components for high temperature applications should ideally be of substantial thickness and oxygen should be excluded whenever possible. A novel suggestion by Knight and Lim is that the overall performance of a rubber of low thermal oxidative resistance will be enhanced by using a surface veneer of a more resistant rubber. In particular, a veneer with a low rate of permeability by oxygen (e.g. Hypalon™, Butyl rubber) would be ideal.

### 2.8.2  Testing

Attempts to predict the life of a product are often based on tests carried out on laboratory samples subjected to accelerated ageing. The test-pieces are usually thin (around 2 mm) and the test temperature considerably higher than the service temperature. It will be realised that the results of such tests will be misleading if the product to be used is substantially thicker since the test-pieces will undergo thermal oxidative degradation. In addition, the loss of antioxidant and plasticiser by volatilisation will be more rapid under the test conditions than from the product in service. Consequently a rubber adequate for certain conditions may be discarded; a more heat-resistant type than is necessary, usually involving higher cost, is then likely to be specified.

### 2.8.3  Interaction of ageing processes

The effects of temperature on the rate of breakdown of rubbers, under aerobic or anaerobic conditions, has been discussed without consideration of other failure mechanisms. The oxidation of rubber may be catalysed by ultraviolet (UV) light, flexing and traces of some metals. In addition, ozone attack of some rubbers, particularly dienes, may occur. The rate at which these forms of ageing take place may be increased as the temperature rises. For example, the degradation of natural rubber by UV light in nitrogen is almost independent of temperature. However, the degradation caused by UV light in air increases with temperature [14].

## 2.9  Conclusions

The ability of a rubber product to withstand exposure to high temperatures is mainly dependent on the nature of the base rubber employed. However, significant improvements in the performance of a product can be obtained by careful selection of the additives incorporated into the rubber, viz. the curing system, filler, plasticiser and protective agent. The rate of degradation (ageing) of an article is also influenced by its size and shape. Misleading information may be given by accelerated ageing tests at elevated temperatures on samples of inappropriate dimensions.

## References

[1]   Knight, G. T. and Lim, H. S. (1975) International Rubber Conference, Kuala Lumper.
[2]   Brydson, J. A. (1978) *Rubber Chemistry*. Elsevier Applied Science, Barking, 70.
[3]   Lee, K. S. and Whelan, A. (ed.) (1981) *Developments in Rubber Technology*, Vol. 2. Elsevier Applied Science, Barking, p. 142.
[4]   Lee, K. S. and Whelan, A. (ed.) (1981) *Developments in Rubber Technology*, Vol. 2. Elsevier Applied Science, Barking, p. 206.
[5]   Lee, K. S. and Whelan, A. (ed.) (1979) *Developments in Rubber Technology*, Vol. 1. Elsevier Applied Science, Barking, p. 74.
[6]   Lee, K. S. and Whelan, A. (ed.) (1979) *Developments in Rubber Technology*, Vol. 1. Elsevier Applied Science, Barking, p. 241.
[7]   Cain, M. E., Knight, G. T., Lewis, P. M. and Saville, B. (1969) *Rubber Res. Inst. Malaysia*, **22**, 289.
[8]   Scott, G. (1977) International Rubber Conference, Brighton.
[9]   Kline, R. H. and Miller, J. P. (1973) *Rubber Chem. Technol.*, **46**, 96.
[10]  Meyer, G. E., Kavchok, R. W. and Naples, F. (1973) *Rubber Chem. Technol.*, **46**, 106.
[11]  Wager, M. P. (1976) *Rubber Chem. Technol.*, **49**, 750.
[12]  Lee, K. S. and Whelan, A. (ed.) (1979) *Developments in Rubber Technology*, Vol. 1. Elsevier Applied Science, Barking, p. 221.
[13]  Lee, K. S. and Whelan, A. (ed.) (1979) *Developments in Rubber Technology*, Vol. 1. Elsevier Applied Science, Barking, p. 258.
[14]  Murakami, K. and Takasugi, S. (1977) *J. Appl. Polym. Sci.*, **21**, 55.
[15]  Thomas, D. K. and Sinnott, R. (1969). *J.I.R.I.*, **3**.
[16]  Mirza, J. and Thormer, H. J. (1985) *Caoutch. Plast.*, 657.
[17]  Mirza, J. and Thormer, H. J. (1985) *Caoutch. Plast.*, 651.
[18]  Lee, K. S. and Whelan, A. (ed.) (1979) *Developments in Rubber Technology*. Elsevier Applied Science, Barking.
[19]  MRPRA, *NR Technical Bulletin*, Malaysia.
[20]  Durham Chemical, *Technical Bulletin*, ARI, England.
[21]  MRPRA, (ed. A. D. Roberts), (1988) *Natural Rubber Science and Technology*. Oxford University Press.

# 3  Thermoplastic elastomers
M. S. M. ALGER

## 3.1 Introduction

Several important industries, namely the plastics, rubber, fibre, coating and adhesive industries, are based on polymer materials. Although the basic properties of the products of these industries all depend on the unique characteristics of polymers, for historical, technical and marketing reasons these industries have largely developed separately. In each case the products are obtained by processing polymer based materials in either a melt or liquid (usually solution) form. Both rubber and plastics products are normally produced by melt processing, whereas solution processing is much more important in fibre, coating and adhesive manufacture. Plastics and rubber products are often of a similar physical form; indeed it is not clear whether some products such as hose or wire and cable coverings should be regarded as plastics or rubber products and whether the materials on which they are based should be considered as plastics or rubbers. Despite these common factors the rubber and plastics industries have grown up separately and have largely remained separate—indeed many plastics and rubber technologists see the two industries as rivals.

The major difference between rubbers and plastics is related to their mechanical behaviour and the mechanical behaviour of the polymers from which they are manufactured. Compared with plastics, rubbers are much softer—typically they have a tensile modulus lower by a factor of about $10^3$—and exhibit much greater elongations from which recovery is usually complete, that is they exhibit rubber elasticity. A further important difference is the necessity for cross-linking the polymer molecules in rubbers by vulcanisation, a process not required in plastics. It is this which has been the main reason for the different emphases in the manufacturing methods used for rubbers and plastics. The need for vulcanisation has always been a central consideration in all aspects of rubber technology—in formulation, compounding and processing.

These differences account for the separate development of the rubber and plastics industries and of the materials on which they are based. Considering the whole range of polymers, however, it must be recognised that there can be no sharp division between rubbery polymers and plastic polymers, but rather that there is a continuous spectrum of material behaviour. This has long been apparent and is exemplified by plasticised polyvinyl chloride (PVC) which was first developed in the early 1930s. The nature of PVC can be altered from that of a relatively stiff plastic to that of a fairly soft rubber by varying the amount of plasticiser used. More recently, ethylene-vinyl acetate (EVA) provides another example where softness and rubberiness can be altered by varying the vinyl acetate content of the copolymer. Thus, from the materials viewpoint, the plastics and rubber industries have much in common. Moreover, there is also much in common from the processing viewpoint and this has become especially apparent with the increasing use of injection moulding in the rubber industry. Since the technologies of the rubber and plastics industries are becoming closer, it is surprising that the industries continue to remain separately organised.

Perhaps the single most important factor that could bring about the integration of the plastics and rubber industries is the development of the group of materials, the *thermoplastic elastomers*, the subject of this chapter. In addition to their direct technical and economic benefits, these may also benefit the polymer industries indirectly by helping to break down the somewhat artificial barriers that still exist between the rubber and plastics industries.

The term thermoplastic elastomer (often abbreviated to TPE), or thermoplastic rubber (TPR), is used to describe those polymer materials which are elastomeric—in that they demonstrate at least a moderate degree of rubber elasticity—but which can be shaped into useful products by thermoplastics processing techniques without vulcanisation to form chemical cross-links between the polymer molecules. The term first came into use with the introduction of the styrene–butadiene–styrene block copolymers in 1965.

The elasticity of rubber derives from the flexibility of the rubber polymer chains, which in turn results from the ease of bond rotation about main chain bonds. This flexibility leads to ready deformation combined with rapid recovery as the stretched molecules revert to their natural randomly coiled state when the deforming force is removed. However, in rubbers for practical technological use, it is necessary to lightly cross-link the polymer chains in order to reduce any permanent change in shape (set or creep) that may occur on stressing, to increase strength and stiffness and to improve resistance to swelling by contacting liquids, especially oils. In conventional rubbers, the cross-links are covalent chemical bonds whose formation requires careful compounding with vulcanisation ingredients followed by heating, most frequently in a mould, to 'set' the shape produced during moulding or other shaping process. In contrast, in thermoplastics shaping processes, no such ingredients are needed and the shape is set simply by cooling the shaped melt to harden it—a simpler and more economic process.

The cross-links in TPEs are not conventional covalent bonds but are 'physical' cross-links formed when the polymer melt is cooled. TPEs therefore offer the ability to manufacture rubbery products by the more convenient

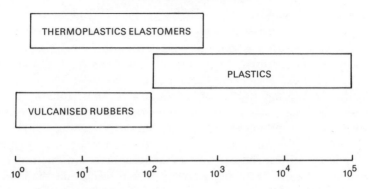

**Figure 3.1** Tensile moduli (MPa) of polymers.

thermoplastics processing methods, saving both compounding and processing costs. The specific advantages that arise from using these methods, compared with the use of traditional rubber processing methods, include shorter cycle times, low die swell, ability to mould to tight tolerances, no flash production, no necessity for trimming and, perhaps most importantly, the ability to re-use scrap material. Overall, a greater uniformity of product quality is more easily achieved in these continuous processes compared with the batchwise processes often used with conventional rubbers.

Given this major commercial advantage, it is hardly surprising that the growth in the use of TPEs has been quite dramatic since their introduction and is at present the fastest materials growth sector among all rubbers. Despite this increasing importance of TPEs, the growth in their usage has not fulfilled initial, though with hindsight perhaps somewhat optimistic, forecasts made in the early days of TPEs. Several factors have combined to limit the growth, one being the limited resistance of TPEs to elevated temperature and to oils, especially in the earlier and cheaper materials. Perhaps the most important reason has been the reluctance of rubber processors to invest in the new plastics processing machinery required for TPEs. Whilst it is true that the plastics processors could adopt TPEs and indeed have done so quite extensively, a lack of knowledge of rubber product markets by the plastics industry has inhibited this development. Furthermore, the TPEs do not fill any gap in the physical property spectrum of rubbers or soft plastics, as may be seen from the tensile modulus in Figure 3.1. Although, in total, TPEs span almost the whole range of stiffnesses of rubbers and the softer plastics, most grades of material would be considered as relatively hard rubbers.

## 3.2 Origin of the physical cross-links in TPEs

The desirable TPE combination of melt processability and solid rubberiness results from the formation of the physical cross-links (also called 'virtual

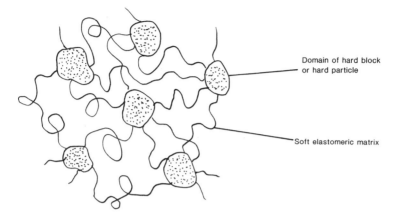

Domain of hard block
or hard particle

Soft elastomeric matrix

**Figure 3.2** Schematic TPE phase structure.

cross-links') between the linear polymer chains when the melt is cooled, and their disappearance when the material is heated for processing, i.e. thermally reversible cross-links. When TPEs are heated, the physical cross-links are destroyed if the temperature is raised above the $T_g$ of the hard phase (or the $T_m$ if crystalline) and the material becomes melt-processable as a thermoplastic. Conversely, on cooling from the melt the hard phase reforms below the $T_g$ or $T_m$. Conventionally vulcanised rubbers have a thermoset network structure of polymer chains permanently cross-linked through chemical covalent bonds. TPEs are two-phase materials usually of a soft rubbery matrix phase containing the second dispersed phase of a harder material. It is the hard phase 'particles' that provide the physical cross-links. This two-phase morphology can be achieved in two ways: either by the use of a block copolymer or of a polymer blend. In either type, the long sequences of polymer repeat units of one variety (whether present in a block of a block copolymer or in a separate polymer molecule in a blend), for the thermodynamic reasons discussed in Chapter 1, are not compatible with the long sequences of the other variety. Phase separation therefore occurs producing the dispersed phase particles or domains, as drawn in Figure 3.2. The domains are often spherical but may have different morphologies such as cylindrical, lamellar or network. The precise morphology depends on the blend or block copolymer composition and its thermal and shear—and therefore processing—history. Since TPE physical properties depend on morphology these too are processing history dependent and may be anisotropic.

For the hard dispersed phase to act as cross-links for the rubbery matrix, the polymer molecular chain sequences of the dispersed phase must themselves have greatly restricted chain motions, and be capable of restricting gross

chain motions of the rubbery chains by interacting with them. In block
copolymers this interaction is provided by the covalent bonds between the
rubbery and hard plastic blocks; in polymer blends the interaction consists of
intermolecular interactions between the two polymers in the interfacial
region. Other types of attraction resulting in effects similar to these physical
cross-links are found in certain polymers sometimes considered as TPEs.
These include ionic attractive forces in ionomers, hydrogen bonding in
plasticised PVC and polyethylene crystallinity in EVA.

## 3.3 The commercial development of TPEs

The concept of thermoplastic elastomers originated with the commercial
introduction of the styrene–butadiene–styrene (SBS) triblock copolymers in
1965 by Shell, though some earlier polyurethane materials were subsequently
also recognised as TPEs. Later, other related styrene linear triblock copolymers with improved properties were developed by Shell. Philips, followed
later by other companies, introduced styrene–butadiene radial copolymers.
Collectively these materials are known as the styrenics and, in tonnage terms,
are the most important group of TPEs.

A different approach to TPE behaviour emerged in 1972 with the
introduction of blends of a crystalline olefin plastic (usually polypropylene)
with an ethylene–propylene rubber (usually EPDM). These materials are
known collectively as thermoplastic olefin rubbers (TPO). In the USA,
polymer manufacturers initially marketed these blends but subsequently the
business was continued by specialist compounders. In contrast in Europe, the
polymer manufacturers continue to be the main suppliers of TPOs. The
TPOs have a better high temperature performance than the styrenics but, like
the styrenics, still have poor compression set and oil resistance.

More recently the emphasis has been on TPOs in which the rubber
becomes extensively vulcanised during compounding with the polypropylene
(sometimes this technique is known as dynamic vulcanisation) to produce
TPOs with much better compression set resistance. This process was
pioneered by Monsanto with Santoprene™ introduced in 1981 and several
other companies have subsequently launched similar materials. These
materials are often known as thermoplastic vulcanisates (TPVs) and seem
likely to replace in large part the older, less satisfactory simple PP/EPDM
blends.

Other polyolefine based materials which have been introduced recently are
Dupont's Alcryn™ and polypropylene/natural rubber blends.

The styrenic and TPO/TPV materials may be considered to be the general
purpose TPEs. Another group of three further types of TPE with superior
strength, toughness and oil and solvent resistance are often referred to as the
engineering TPEs. In general these materials are available only in harder
grades and are 2–5 times more expensive. The engineering TPEs are all block,

**Table 3.1** Consumption and general properties of TPEs

| Type | USA consumption (1987) | | W. Europe consumption (1986) | |
| --- | --- | --- | --- | --- |
| | Tonnes | % | Tonnes | % |
| Styrenics | 92 000 | 48 | 78 000 | 52 |
| TPO/TPV | 62 000 | 33 | 27 000 | 18 |
| TPU | 25 000 | 13 | 28 500 | 19 |
| Polyester | 11 000 | 6 | 9000 | 6 |
| TOTAL | 190 000 | | 142 500 | |

**Table 3.2** General properties of TPEs

| Type | Hardness range (shore) | Approximate relative price range* | Specific gravity range |
| --- | --- | --- | --- |
| Styrenic (uncompounded) | 30A–90A | 1.0–2.2 | 0.91–0.94 |
| TPO/TPV | 60A–75D | 0.8–1.8 | 0.90–1.1 |
| TPU | 70A–70D | 2.2–2.8 | 1.05–1.25 |
| Polyester | 35D–75D | 2.5–3.5 | 1.15–1.45 |
| Polyamide | 75A–65D | 2.6–5.0 | 1.0 –1.15 |

* 1.0 represents approximately £1500 per tonne (1988).

often multiblock, copolymers in which the hard blocks are crystalline so that melt processing takes place above the crystalline melting point. The first of these materials were the thermoplastic polyurethanes (TPUs; Goodrich 1958) though subsequently many other companies have marketed TPUs. Next came the polyester materials (DuPont 1972) followed by the polyamide block copolymers in the late 1970s.

Currently total TPE consumption is about 0.5 million tonnes worldwide (about 0.15 million tonnes in Western Europe) representing about 8% of total synthetic rubber consumption. Forecasts suggest that TPE consumption will continue to grow at 5–10% per annum (compared with about 2% for all rubbers) into the 1990s.

The relative importance of the main TPE types illustrated by the recent tonnage consumption figures is shown in Table 3.1 and some of their main characteristics are shown in Table 3.2. The range of hardness values available is shown in Figure 3.3.

## 3.4 Styrenics

### 3.4.1 Structures

Styrenics were the original TPEs and are still the most important group in tonnage terms. Total worldwide consumption is about 0.3 million tonnes

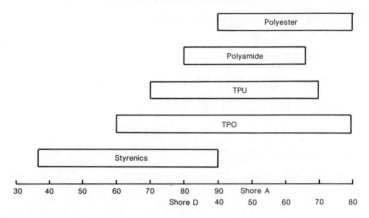

**Figure 3.3** Hardness range of TPE.

which is about 50% of total TPE consumption in the USA and Western Europe. There are several different styrene–elastomer block copolymers which make up the styrenics: the elastomer is a diene and the copolymer has a linear triblock structure styrene–diene–styrene. The styrene–butadiene–styrene (SBS) copolymers were the first to be introduced by Shell in 1965 and are the most important. They are marketed as Kraton D™ in the USA and as Cariflex TR™ in Europe. A typical structure for SBS is

styrene  –  butadiene  –  styrene
MW 15 000    MW 70 000    MW 15 000

giving a total molecular weight of 100 000, which is relatively low for a rubber. Similar styrene–isoprene–styrene (SIS) polymers are produced, but these have lower styrene contents and are therefore softer. SBS and SIS polymers are also produced by Enichem (previously Anic™ and Enoxy™) as Europrene Sol T™, and SBS is produced by Asahi as Tufprene™ and Asaprene™. Shell also produce a range of styrene–ethylene/butylene–styrene copolymers (SEBS; Kraton G™ and Elexar™). Styrene–butadiene diblock copolymers are also produced and although they do not have the desirable mechanical behaviour associated with triblock polymers they are sometimes compounded with them. Radial, or star, styrene–butadiene (SB) copolymers of the type $(S-B)_n X$ were produced by Philips (Solprene™) but are now produced by Petrofina (Finaprene™) and by Shell (Kraton™ or Cariflex TR™). The structures of these different types are represented in Figure 3.4.

Styrenic polymers are produced by the anionic living polymerisation technique. This involves sequential polymerisation of the styrene followed by the butadiene, followed by coupling of the chain ends using a suitable coupling agent. A difunctional agent gives a linear triblock polymer, tri-

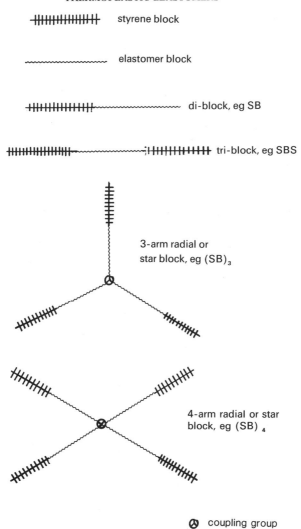

Figure 3.4 Structures of styrenic block copolymers.

functional a three-arm and tetrafunctional a four-arm branched polymer etc.

The SEBS polymers are produced by hydrogenation of SBS. This removes the unsaturation and hence improves resistance to thermal oxidation and weathering. The polymers are named styrene–ethylene/butylene–styrene since the elastomeric block consists of a random copolymer of ethylene and butylene units arising from two different isomeric types of butadiene unit. The 1,4- type gives two ethylene units on hydrogenation:

$$-CH_2-CH{=}CH-CH_2- \longrightarrow -CH_2-CH_2-CH_2-CH_2-$$

and the 1,2- type gives a butylene unit:

$$-CH_2-CH- \longrightarrow -CH_2-CH-$$
$$\underset{\underset{CH_2}{\overset{\|}{CH}}}{|} \qquad \underset{\underset{CH_3}{\overset{|}{CH_2}}}{|}$$

### 3.4.2 Effects of morphology

In styrenics, the styrene end blocks aggregate together and phase separate from the elastomeric block material (which comprises the continuous matrix) to form dispersed polystyrene domains. Owing to their high $T_g$ (about 95°C) these domains provide the physical cross-links. The morphology of the two-phase system has been extensively studied by transmission electron microscopy of thin sections with osmium staining of the elastomer phase to improve contrast between the phases. This work has revealed phase morphologies of a surprising variety, sometimes of great regularity which has fascinated polymer scientists since the staining technique was introduced in 1967. Such studies have provided direct experimental evidence for the earlier suggestion that dispersed *spherical* polystyrene domains are formed in typical commercial copolymers of about 30% styrene content (Figure 3.5). However other morphologies, such as cylindrical and lamellar, are also found dependent on styrene content, block lengths and sample preparation method.

Although many of these studies have been directed by academic interests, they have provided an explanation for the effects of processing on phase structure and mechanical behaviour (including anisotropy) found commercially. Some of these effects are illustrated in Table 3.3.

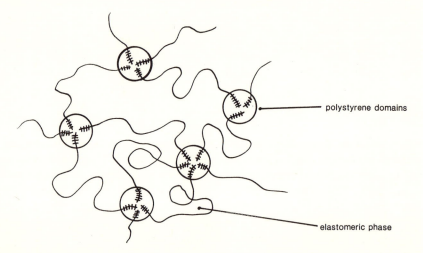

polystyrene domains

elastomeric phase

**Figure 3.5** Styrene block copolymer morphology.

**Table 3.3** Effects of processing on radial SBS morphology and properties

| Processing conditions | Morphology | Initial tensile modulus (MPa) |
|---|---|---|
| Injection moulding | Randomly fibrillar | 11.0 |
| Extrusion at 20 rpm: | | |
| machine direction | Highly oriented fibrils | 23.0 |
| transverse direction | | 6.6 |
| Extrusion at 40 rpm: | | |
| machine direction | Poorly oriented fibrils | 11.0 |
| transverse direction | | 6.8 |
| Calendering: | | |
| machine direction | Randomly fibrillar | 12.0 |
| transverse direction | | 11.5 |
| Casting from cyclohexane solution | Polystyrene cylinders | 6.5 |

### 3.4.3 Response to temperature

The softening of TPEs at elevated temperature is determined by the $T_g$ of the hard blocks. Although polystyrene $T_g$ is about 100°C for high molecular weight polymer, for the lower molecular weights found in styrenic TPE blocks the $T_g$ is much lower so that softening occurs at much lower temperatures. This limits the upper service life temperature to about 65°C in stressed products, though it may be somewhat higher in non-stressed applications. Thermal softening is responsible for the excessive creep or set that occurs at elevated temperatures, one of the main limitations of these materials. In contrast, low temperature performance is very good: flexibility is retained quite well since it depends on the $T_g$ of the elastomeric blocks. This is about $-60$°C with isoprene and ethylene/butylene and about $-90$°C with butadiene blocks.

### 3.4.4 Mechanical behaviour

The styrenics are available in a wide range of hardnesses, from 35 Shore A to

**Table 3.4** Properties of uncompounded styrenics (Shell Kraton™ polymers)

| Polymer | Styrene content % | Shore A hardness | 300% modulus MPa | Tensile strength MPa | Elongation % |
|---|---|---|---|---|---|
| Linear SBS | 31 | 71 | 2.76 | 31.7 | 880 |
| Linear SBS | 17 | 53 | 0.93 | 4.83 | 1100 |
| Linear SIS | 14 | 37 | 0.69 | 21.4 | 1300 |
| Linear SIS | 21 | 52 | 1.38 | 20.0 | 1200 |
| Branched (SB)$_n$ | 21 | 65 | 2.42 | 31.7 | 900 |
| Branched (SB)$_n$ | 30 | 75 | 5.52 | 27.6 | 820 |
| Branched (SI)$_n$ | 10 | 32 | 0.69 | 8.62 | 1300 |

55 Shore D, the hardness increasing as the styrene content increases from about 25% to about 50% in commercial TPEs. (At about 75% styrene content the products are hard thermoplastics, as with Philips K-Resin™.) The styrene domains contribute to hardness, not only by providing the physical cross-links but also by acting as reinforcing filler particles. Additional reinforcing fillers therefore are not used. In general SIS materials which contain the least styrene (15–20%), are the softest, whilst SEBS materials are the hardest. Some properties of typical uncompounded copolymers are shown in Table 3.4.

### 3.4.5 Melt viscosity

The melt viscosities of the styrenics are higher than those of the corresponding homopolymer polybutadiene or polystyrene of similar molecular weight. This is most likely to be a result of the persistence of the domain structure in the melt, though of course the polystyrene domains are softened at the processing temperatures used (150°–200°C). The melts show a greater shear rate dependency (non-Newtonian behaviour), molecular weight dependency and elasticity than the homopolymers. The branched (star) polymers have lower viscosities in both melt and solution than the linear polymers of equivalent molecular weight.

### 3.4.6 Other properties

The elastomeric blocks in SBS and SIS are unsaturated and therefore are sensitive to oxidation, with poor thermal oxidative and weathering resistance in these TPEs. In SEBS, the elastomeric blocks are saturated and these materials show much improved oxidation resistance. They are therefore preferred for higher temperature and outdoor applications. The polymers themselves are colourless and allow products in a wide range of colours to be produced; optically transparent products are also possible.

Together with the TPOs, the styrenics are the lowest cost materials, with SIS polymers costing about 15% more and SEBS up to 100% more than SBS.

### 3.4.7 Effects of compounding

Unlike most other TPEs, the styrenics are not used in uncompounded form. Indeed commercial compounds usually contain only 25–50% of block copolymer. Thus the styrenics have the advantage of a wide range of compounding possibilities resulting in a wide range of applications as well as reductions in costs.

Polystyrene homopolymer is frequently added both to produce stiffer materials and as a processing aid. Processing oils are used to decrease hardness and to improve processability. The oils must be compatible with the

**Table 3.5** Typical formulations for styrenic products (values in phr)

| Ingredient | Sports shoe sole | Crepe shoe sole | Wire/cable insulation | Sound-deadening material |
|---|---|---|---|---|
| SBS | 100 | 100 | — | — |
| SEBS | — | — | 100 | 100 |
| Polystyrene | 80–100 | 15–25 | — | — |
| Polyolefin | — | — | 100–125 | 80–120 |
| Filler | 50–80 | 10–30 | 50–80 | 500–1000 |
| Oil | 90–110 | 100–130 | 75–125 | 100–140 |
| Heat stabiliser | 0.8 | 0.8 | 1.0 | 0.5 |

elastomeric phase but must not interact with the polystyrene domains, otherwise the material is severely weakened and the softening point is reduced. Hence oils rich in aromatics are avoided: naphthenic oils are used with SBS and paraffinic oils with SEBS. Other polymers are often compounded with the styrenics. Polyethylene and EVA are used in SBS to improve solvent and ozone resistance, whereas polypropylene is used in SEBS. Here even small amounts of polypropylene can raise the softening point considerably since it forms a continuous network even at low loadings. Cheap inert fillers, such as calcium carbonate, clays and talc, may also be used in quite high loadings without deterioration of the mechanical behaviour. Reinforcing fillers are rarely used. A non-staining antioxidant such as a hindered phenol or thioester is frequently required to prevent degradation during processing (and reprocessing) and service life.

Examples of typical compound formulations are shown in Table 3.5 and of compound properties in Table 3.6.

## 3.4.8 Applications

Three areas of application developed rapidly after the styrenics were first introduced: shoe solings, adhesives and bitumen additives. Though these still remain the most important applications, recent growth in usage has been in other areas such as wire and cable covering, polymer blending as impact

**Table 3.6** Typical properties of styrenic compounds

| Material | Specific gravity | Shore hardness | Tensile strength MPa | 100% modulus MPa | Elongation % |
|---|---|---|---|---|---|
| General purpose | 1.0 | 65A | 5.9 | 3.3 | 500 |
| Shoe sole | 1.0 | 47A | 3.9 | 1.9 | 550 |
| Wire/cable covering | 1.0 | 80A | 14.0 | 4.1 | 500 |
| Sound deadening | 1.94 | 36D | 4.8 | 3.5 | 250 |
| Medical | 0.9 | 55A | 7.6 | 1.7 | 700 |

modifiers and in automotive products, especially using the higher performance SEBS materials. As moulded and extruded products, the styrenics are often used as replacements for plasticised PVC or EPDM. In shoe soling, the particular advantages of SBS are its good frictional properties, low temperature flexibility and ability to be injection moulded readily.

The SEBS materials with their greater heat stability have found a wider range of applications, especially more recently in automotive products such as electrical wire insulation and sound insulation materials. An interesting exploitation of the processability of TPEs compared with conventionally vulcanised rubbers is the possibility of coextrusion with a more rigid plastic to provide, for example, a soft sealing edge to a stiffer component, as in window sealing strips and ventilator flaps.

For adhesives use, a major advantage is the ease of application to the substrate either as a solvent-based or hot melt adhesive. Styrenics, with a relatively low molecular weight compared with conventional rubbers, have a high solubility and rapid solution rates in many solvents such as toluene and methylethyl ketone. However, hot melt adhesives are the more important. As with moulded and extruded products, the polymer is usually compounded with relatively large amounts of additives, particularly synthetic resins and oils. Compatibility considerations, especially with the elastomeric blocks, determine the choice of these additives. The polyterpenes are used with SIS polymer, whereas hydrocarbon resins, paraffin oils and polybutenes are used with SBS and SEBS. Pressure-sensitive adhesives—mostly as hot melt adhesives—are the most important products, especially for tapes and labels. Because low softness is required, polystyrene contents are kept low and quantities of soft styrene—butadiene diblock polymer can be incorporated, since these adhesives are non-load bearing. Assembly adhesives are harder and have lower tack. SEBS copolymers are also used in hot melts as sealants, as formed in place gaskets and in cable filling, and as solutions in building applications.

Styrenics are used in blends because they show an unusually high compatibility with a wide range of other polymers. This, together with their thermoplastic nature, make them attractive materials for blending with other polymers. One of their major uses is as a modifier for bitumens, especially to modify their thermal properties. They not only improve the low temperature flexibility but also raise the softening point, thus reducing flow in roofing and paving materials whilst increasing strength, ductility and recovery but retaining low melt viscosity. Even low additions, about 5%, are effective since the block copolymer is capable of forming a network structure in the bitumen. SBS is widely used in road surface dressings and water proofings because of its low cost, but SEBS is often preferred for roofing because of its better weatherability.

Styrenics, like other rubbers, are also used as blends with a wide range of thermoplastic polymers as impact modifiers. However, because they are not

**Table 3.7** Effect of functionalised SEBS on Nylon 66

| % SEBS by weight | Izod impact strength J/m | Flexural modulus MPa |
|---|---|---|
| 0 | 60 | 3000 |
| 5 | 100 | 2875 |
| 10 | 250 | 2625 |
| 15 | 625 | 2350 |
| 20 | 950 | 2020 |

vulcanised and have low melt viscosities, they are easier to disperse and can be simply blended, even directly in an injection moulding machine. They are usually used in polystyrene and related polymers, especially in high impact polystyrene for super-tough and fire-resistant grades. Other uses are for the improvement of low temperature performance of polypropylene and in polyethylene films for the improvement of tear and impact strengths. In a more recent development, styrenics are used as impact modifiers in engineering plastics such as PPO and polycarbonate. Here SEBS is preferred because of its greater heat stability. Most recently, special grades have been introduced with improved compatibility with more polar polymers such as nylons and polybutylene terephthalate. This is achieved by grafting a further more polar, monomer, such as maleic or succinic anhydride, often called the functional monomer. An example of what can be achieved by this is shown in Table 3.7.

In addition to acting as impact modifiers in blends, the styrenics and functionalised styrenics can act as compatibilisers for blends of other polymers, improving the interfacial bonding between polymer pairs which would otherwise be poorly adhering. This has considerable potential for improving the properties of mixed scrap and waste polymers.

## 3.5 Polyesters

### 3.5.1 Introduction

Engineering TPEs were introduced in 1972 by DuPont (as Hytrel™), as engineering materials which offered a range of properties superior to other TPEs. They combine high strength with low temperature flexibility and excellent resistance to oils and other liquids. However, at £3.00–£4.00 per kg, they are considerably more expensive that most other TPEs. Despite this high cost they may often replace other rubbers because of the ease with which products may be manufactured. Similar materials were introduced by Toyobo (Pelprene™) and Akzo (Arnitel™). More recently several other manufacturers have entered the market—General Electric (Lomod™), Gaf (Gaflex™, now produced by Hoechst–Celanese as Riteflex™) and Montedison (Pibiflex™).

### 3.5.2 Structure

Like other engineering TPEs, the polyester polymer chains are multiblock copolymers of alternating soft and hard blocks of the general type $-(AB)_x-$. They are also referred to as segmented copolymers and the blocks as hard and soft segments. Usually the soft segments are polyether blocks so that the materials are known as polyetherester copolymers. In some grades of Arnitel and Pelprene the soft blocks are also polyester (polyesterester copolymer). A typical structure is

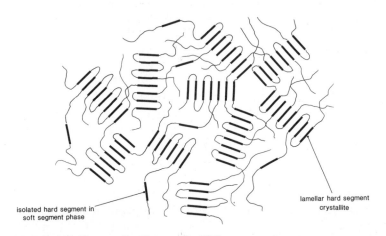

The amorphous soft segments are polytetramethyleneglycol terephthalate (PTMGT) blocks with the polyether having a molecular weight of about 1000. The hard segments are polytetramethylene terephthalate (4GT) units (also called polybutylene terephthalate, PBT) which are at least 10 units long and capable of crystallising. The lamellar crystals of the hard blocks, which act as the physical cross-links, appear to form a network structure as shown in Figure 3.6, which probably accounts for the exceptional strength properties. Overall the molecular weight is about 30 000, giving low melt viscosities and easy processing.

### 3.5.3 Properties

The polyether segments have a $T_g$ of about $-50°C$ whilst the hard segments melt in the range $170°-250°C$, the $T_m$ increasing as hardness, i.e. hard block content, increases. This gives the polyesters a combination of retention of

**Figure 3.6** Schematic diagram of semi-crystalline TPEs.

**Table 3.8** Properties of polyester TPE (Hytrel™)

| | | | | |
|---|---|---|---|---|
| Hardness (Shore D) | 40 | 55 | 63 | 72 |
| Specific gravity | 1.17 | 1.20 | 1.22 | 1.25 |
| $T_m$(°C) | 170 | 220 | 214 | 232 |
| Vicat softening point (°C) | 112 | 180 | 184 | 203 |
| Tensile strength (MPa) | 30 | 44 | 44 | 52 |
| Flexural modulus (MPa) | 48 | 207 | 345 | 517 |
| Elongation (%) | 560 | 560 | 440 | 420 |

flexibility at low temperature with high softening point. However, in common with other polyesters, hydrolysis resistance at elevated temperatures is limited. For use at above 70°C in contact with water the addition of a heat stabiliser is recommended. This is often a carbodiimide used as a masterbatch. For dry heat use, special heat stabilised grades are available which, for the harder grades, are suitable for use at up to about 180°C for long periods. It is claimed that the polyesterester materials have superior heat resistance to the polyetheresters. Overall a wider temperature range of use is possible than with the other TPEs.

The polyesters are available only in the harder range of TPE hardnesses of Shore 35D to 75D, corresponding to a hard block content of about 30–85%. Compared with the somewhat similar TPU materials, the polyesters have higher modulus values at the same hardness. Like the TPUs, they offer the best range of strength properties in terms of tear strength, tensile strength, flex life and abrasion resistance. A typical range of mechanical properties is shown in Table 3.8. The polyesters also exhibit outstanding oil resistance, the best of all being TPEs, especially at elevated temperatures. Significant attack does not occur until perhaps 150°C is reached, though petrol resistance is restricted to about 70°C. Resistance to polar liquids is also good, especially in the harder grades.

The polymers are melt processable by a full range of thermoplastics processing methods—injection moulding, extrusion (including blown film) and blow moulding. The last technique requires the use of special grades with high melt strength. Melt temperature depends on the hardness of the grade and increases from 170°C to 250°C as the hardness increases. Though the melts have good heat stability (up to 250°C), it is important that the moisture content is kept below 0.1% otherwise hydrolytic degradation becomes significant. Since polyesters absorb moisture from the atmosphere the polymer should be dried before processing, unless it is stored in a sealed container.

### 3.5.4 Applications

The uses of polyesters are limited by their comparatively high cost, but their use is justified when superior strength and oil or heat resistance are required.

The cost may be offset by the use of thinner sections (and hence less polymer) than is required with lower performance rubbers. A good example of this is the increasing use of polyesters as a replacement for Neoprene in automotive protective bellows for steering mechanisms and constant velocity joints. This important application also makes use of the excellent flex fatigue life.

Polyesters have a further use as high pressure hose liners and covers when good solvent and abrasion resistance is required, as with oil rig and paint sprayer hose. Polyesters are also useful for cables, having excellent chemical and oil resistance for optical fibre and automotive cables. Other recent automotive uses include body panels (often paintable without the need of a primer coat), bumper fascias, spoilers, exterior trim and for noise damping. Other applications include silent running gear wheels, pump diaphragms, bearings and seals.

## 3.6 Thermolastic polyurethanes (TPU)

### 3.6.1 Introduction

Polyurethanes (PU), i.e. polymers containing urethane groups —O—CO—NH— in the polymer molecular chains, are the polymers most versatile in their commercial applications. Product types vary from soft rubbers to hard plastics, fibres, coatings and adhesive materials. Elastomeric polyurethanes have been available since the 1940s whilst relatively hard plastics were developed in the 1950s. Softer, more rubbery but thermoplastic materials were described by Goodrich in 1958 (Estane™), which are now recognised as the first TPE materials. Soon after this several other companies developed TPU materials—Mobay (Texin™), Upjohn (Pellethane™, now produced by Dow), Bayer (Desmopan™) and Elastogran (Elastollan™ and Caprolan™). Subsequently many other producers appeared: Cyanamid (Cytor™), Dunlop (Jectothane™), Hooker (Rucothane™), Ohio (Orthane™), Quinn (Q-Thane™), Thiokol (Plastothane™) and Uniroyal (Roylar™). The TPUs are the oldest established TPEs with the most mature markets. It is not surprising therefore that their growth is forecast to be less than for other TPEs.

The TPUs are engineering TPEs since they are hard, high strength (especially with respect to abrasion resistance) and oil resistant materials. Overall they are rather similar in their behaviour to the polyester TPEs.

### 3.6.2 Structure

Polyurethane molecules are formed by reaction of a diisocyanate (OCN–R–NCO) with a polyol, i.e. a substance containing more than one hydroxyl group. Thus a diol, HO—R'—OH, will produce a linear polyurethane. TPUs, like the polyesters, are linear multiblock (or segmented) copolymers of alternating soft and hard segments. The soft segments are formed by reaction of a diisocyanate with a long chain diol. They are linked together through the hard segments by reaction of the diisocyanate with a short chain diol as chain extender. Many variations of each of the reactants is possible, but in most TPU production the isocyanate is 4,4′-diphenylmethane diisocyanate (MDI) and the chain extender is 1,4-butane diol. However there is much variation in the choice of long chain diol used. It is a low molecular weight prepolymer of molecular weight 600–4000 and may be a polyester (giving a polyesterurethane) or a polyether (giving a polyetherurethane) terminated with hydroxyl groups. Commonly used diols are polyethylene adipate and polycaprolactone (PCL) glycol ester polyesters and polytetramethylene glycol and polypropylene glycol polyethers. A typical molecular structure is:

As with the polyester TPEs, the hard and soft segments are incompatible and phase separation occurs with the hard segments forming crystalline domains dispersed in an elastomeric matrix of soft segment material. The hard segment domains act as the physical cross-links which break down at temperatures above the melting temperature of the crystals, thus making the TPUs melt processable as thermoplastics.

### 3.6.3 Properties

Commercial TPUs are available in a wider range of hardnesses (from Shore A70 to D85) than with the polyesters. This range corresponds to a 100% modulus range of 23–30 MPa and to a tensile strength range of 25–70 MPa. A typical range of properties is shown in Table 3.9.

TPUs have commendable strength properties. They have outstandingly high tear strength and abrasion resistance, as well as good oil resistance. The polyesterurethanes are superior to the polyether materials, but the polyethers retain their low temperature flexibility better. Soft segment $T_g$ values are about $-50°C$.

The hard segment crystalline regions show a $T_m$ of 170°–230°C, the value increasing with increasing hardness, and processing temperatures are thus

**Table 3.9** Properties of thermoplastic polyurethanes (Desmopan™)

| | | | | |
|---|---|---|---|---|
| Hardness (Shore D) | 32 | 40 | 55 | 59 |
| Tensile strength (MPa) | 40 | 45 | 50 | 50 |
| Elongation (%) | 450 | 450 | 400 | 350 |
| 100% Modulus (MPa) | 6.0 | 9.0 | 15.0 | 20.0 |
| Rebound resilience (%) | 42 | 33 | 32 | 33 |

within this range. Upper service life temperatures are about 80°C, or perhaps 120°C with intermittent use (not as high as with polyester TPEs). The polyesterurethanes have a better resistance to dry hot air than the polyethers but have a more limited hydrolysis resistance. This is probably their most serious limitation. As a consequence, care must be taken to ensure that the material is dry before processing otherwise excessive degradation can occur.

The TPUs are polar materials and so they have good oil and fuel resistance, the polyesterurethanes performing better in this respect. Overall the PCL based materials show the best combination of oil and solvent resistance with hydrolytic stability.

### 3.6.4 Applications

The TPUs have established a wide range of uses, especially where their superior strength properties and liquid resistance justifies their high cost. Footwear uses include football boot soles and outer layers of ski boots where a combination of high tear strength, low temperature flexibility, high gloss and colouration are important. In mechanical goods, TPUs find uses as toothed drive belts, couplings and quiet running gears, non-marking castor and trolley wheels and as abrasion-resistant screens for sieving sand, aggregate etc. Wire and cable coverings for use in harsh environments such as oil rigs and for industrial tools, utilise the low temperature flexibility, high abrasion, grease, oil and seawater resistance of TPUs. Fire hose can be made much lighter and less bulky by the use of a TPU inner liner.

There are many automotive uses such as in ball joints, bearing bushes and bellows. More recently, bodyside mouldings with excellent impact resistance especially to stone chips, such as rubbing strips and sill covers, and oil and fuel resistance have become of interest. For these, glass fibre filled materials, with greatly reduced coefficients of thermal expansion, are being used.

## 3.7 Polyamides

### 3.7.1 Introduction

The polyamide elastomers are the most recently developed group of TPEs, the best known materials were introduced by Atochem (Pebax™) in 1981. Other manufacturers are EMS-Chemie (Grilamid ELT™ and Grilon ELX™) and Dow (Estamid™, previously produced by Upjohn). The polyamides are engineering TPEs with especially attractive dynamic properties and hydrolysis resistance.

### 3.7.2 Structure

Like the other engineering TPEs, the polyamides are multiblock segmented copolymers with alternating soft and hard segments. As is usual the two different segment types are incompatible so that phase separation into domains occurs. The soft segments may be polyether (polyetheramide) or polyester (polyesteramide) or be of both types. A wide range of both hard and soft segment types may be used. In the Pebax™ materials, a polyether prepolymer terminated with hydroxyl groups is reacted with a polyamide terminated with carboxyl groups to form the block copolymer. Thus a typical structure is

$$HO-\left[\mathord{\sim\!\!\!\sim\!\!\!\sim\!\!\!\sim\!\!\!\sim\!\!\!\sim}-O-\underset{\underset{O}{\|}}{C}\left(R-NH-\underset{\underset{O}{\|}}{C}\right)_{\!\!x}\right]_{\!\!n}-OH$$

where the amide blocks are nylon 11 or nylon 12. In the EMS polymers, the amide blocks are nylon 6 or nylon 12. In Estamid™, partially aromatic amide blocks are used.

### 3.7.3 Properties

The polyamides are available in a wider range of hardness than the other engineering TPEs, from Shore A60 to D75. Some typical properties are shown in Table 3.10.

The tensile and tear strengths and abrasion resistance are comparable to those of the other engineering TPEs, with impact strength and flexibility retained particularly well at low temperatures ($-40°C$). The dynamic behaviour is particularly good with low hysteresis, high resilience and good flex fatigue.

The polyamide blocks melt at $170°–220°C$ depending on their type, so melt processing is in the range $180°–240°C$. Since polyamides absorb atmospheric moisture, if the materials have been exposed to the atmosphere they must be dried before processing.

In contrast to the other engineering TPEs, the use of fillers such as calcium carbonate, carbon black and glass fibre has been investigated.

### 3.7.4 Applications

Probably the most important use of polyamides is in moulded sportshoe soles for football boots and ski boots. Here, the flexural fatigue resistance, low

**Table 3.10** Properties of polyetheramides (Pebax™)

| | | | | | |
|---|---|---|---|---|---|
| Hardness (Shore D) | 25 | 35 | 40 | 55 | 63 |
| Tensile strength (MPa) | 29 | 34 | 36 | 44 | 51 |
| Elongation (%) | 715 | 710 | 485 | 455 | 380 |
| 25% Modulus (MPa) | 1.85 | 2.35 | 6.5 | 11.9 | 17.6 |
| Tensile modulus (MPa) | 10.4 | 14.6 | 50 | 145 | 260 |
| Tear strength (kN/m) | 38 | 45 | 70 | 115 | 150 |

temperature flexibility and impact strength are all important. Other products include silent running gears, tubing with good flex life and antiscuff and chemical resistant properties, drive belts, protective bellows and electronic keyboard pads.

## 3.8 Thermoplastic polyolefin elastomers (TPO)

### 3.8.1 Introduction

The TPO materials, in tonnage consumption terms, are the second most important group of TPE materials after the styrenics. Like the styrenics, they are low cost but of inferior properties compared to the engineering TPEs Unlike all the other TPE materials, the TPOs are based on polymer blends rather than block copolymers. Most TPOs are blends of polypropylene (PP) and ethylene–propylene–diene monomer rubber (EPDM).

The first TPO material was introduced in 1972 by Uniroyal as TPR (later produced by Reichold, then BP and now by Monsanto). Several other manufacturers soon developed similar materials—DuPont (Somel™), Goodrich (Telcar™), and Exxon (Vistaflex™). Subsequently many other companies entered the field—Montedison (Dutral™), ISR (Uneprene™), DSM (Keltan TP™), Bayer (Levaflex™), Himont (Dutralene™) and Huls (Vestolene EM™). In the USA, the early suppliers were major polymer manufacturers but after a few years manufacture was transferred to compounding companies. In Europe by contrast, the blending operations and supply of TPOs has tended to remain in-house with the polymer manufacturers.

In some of the earlier TPOs, the EPDM component was partially cross-linked. More recently the emphasis has been on materials in which the EPDM has become fully cross-linked during the blending operation—the so-called dynamic vulcanisation process. This was pioneered by Monsanto with Santoprene™ introduced in 1981. Several other companies have recently introduced similar materials—Exxon (Trefsin™), DSM (Kelprox™) and Montedison (Dutral FLX™). These materials are sometimes referred to as thermoplastic vulcanisates (TPV). They are superior to the earlier TPOs in their elastic properties, compression set and oil resistance.

Most recently Monsanto has introduced an especially oil resistant material (Geolast™) which is a blend of PP with nitrile rubber and includes a third copolymer as a compatibilising agent. Certain other polyolefine based materials have also been introduced recently as TPEs, such as DuPont's Alcryn™ and dynamically vulcanised natural rubber (DVNR).

### 3.8.2 Structure

A wide range of commercial materials of various compositions is produced by intensive mixing of PP with EPDM. Blends containing a high proportion of

PP, with the rubber component acting mainly as an impact modifier, are usually considered as plastics materials and are especially important for their use in car bumpers. TPO materials generally contain less than 30% PP.

Since the PP and EPDM are incompatible, the blend has a two-phase structure with the crystalline PP component acting in a similar manner to the hard domains in the block copolymer TPEs. However, the phase structure is complex and varies with PP content and compounding conditions. With more than 50% PP, i.e. in the plastic materials, the PP forms a continuous phase. Below 50% PP, either the PP or the EPDM may be continuous. The correct choice of grade of PP and EPDM is important in order to obtain the required phase structure. Generally a high molecular weight EPDM containing about 70% ethylene with long sequences of ethylene units in the copolymer chain is preferred. This leads to some ethylene crystallisation in the EPDM phase which seems to contribute to the physical cross-linking and hence greater elasticity of the blends with PP. In contrast, a low molecular weight grade of PP is preferred—this helps to keep the melt viscosity low and assists PP crystallisation. In the TPVs, it is claimed that the blending process forms as especially fine dispersion of rubber particles of about 1 μm diameter within a PP matrix, even at relatively high EPDM contents.

### 3.8.3 Properties

Earlier TPOs were available only in the harder grades, but more recently the range of hardness has been extended into the softer range so that now the range of hardnesses available is from Shore A60 to D55. As with other TPEs, the hardness, modulus and tensile strength increase with the hard domain material content which in this case is with the PP component of the blend. Some typical properties of a TPV type of TPO are shown in Table 3.11.

Earlier materials exhibited poor elastic properties, such as lack of recovery and low resilience, especially at elevated temperatures. This limited their use in many applications to below 60°C. Compression and tension set was also excessive, especially in the softer grades. These deficiencies have been greatly overcome in the newer TPV materials, as has the limited oil and solvent resistance.

The rubber phase has a $T_g$ of about $-50°C$ so that flexibility in TPOs is retained to low temperatures. The PP phase has a $T_m$ of about 160°C so that processing melt temperatures are in the range 190°–230°C. Processing by

**Table 3.11** Mechanical properties of cross-linked TPO (Santoprene™)

| | | | | | | | |
|---|---|---|---|---|---|---|---|
| Hardness (Shore) | 55A | 64A | 73A | 80A | 87A | 40D | 50D |
| Tensile strength (MPa) | 4.4 | 6.9 | 8.3 | 11.0 | 15.9 | 19.0 | 27.6 |
| Elongation (%) | 330 | 400 | 375 | 450 | 530 | 600 | 600 |
| 100% Modulus (MPa) | 2.1 | 2.3 | 3.2 | 4.8 | 6.9 | 8.6 | 10.0 |
| Tear strength (kN/m) | 19 | 24.5 | 27.8 | 34.0 | 48.7 | 64.6 | 90.0 |

injection moulding extrusion and blow moulding is readily performed. The TPOs show excellent ozone, weathering and hydrolysis resistance. The TPV varieties have good hot air ageing and may be used to temperatures of about 125°C even for long periods. The low specific gravity, about 0.97, contributes to a low volume cost.

### 3.8.4 Applications

TPOs find a wide range of applications, very often as a replacement for traditionally vulcanised rubbers. As rubber processors' recognition of the need to re-equip with thermoplastics processing equipment increases, the use of TPOs is expected to grow, especially with the newer TPV materials with better elastic properties.

As with other TPEs, there are many uses in automotive applications which include sealing strips (especially interesting are TPO coextrusions with a harder material such as polypropylene), bellows, air ducting and mirror housings. Rubber parts in home and office appliances such as feet, gaskets, hose, seals and handles may be of TPO. In building applications, TPOs are used for window, door and drain seals and electrical applications include wire and cable insulations and coverings.

### 3.9 Summary

Since the introduction of TPEs nearly 25 years ago, their desirable combination of rubbery properties and thermoplastic processability has come to be increasingly appreciated. It is also more readily recognised that despite their higher materials cost compared with traditional vulcanised rubbers, final product cost using TPE may be lower because of the more favourable economics of their processing.

Some of their earlier deficiencies, such as high compression and tension set and lack of elastic recovery compared with traditionally vulcanised rubbers, are being overcome in many of the newer materials. Thus, in the two most important general purpose types—the styrenics and TPOs—considerable performance improvements have been achieved with the development of the SEBS and TPV materials respectively. Furthermore, the range of high performance, though more costly, engineering TPEs continues to widen. These developments in improved materials should ensure sustained healthy growth in the usage of TPEs as they open up new areas of application, especially in the automotive industry.

### Further reading

Elias, H.-G. and Vohwinkel, F. (ed.) (1986) *New Commercial Polymers 2*. Gordon and Breach, New York.

Folkes, M. J. (ed.) (1985) *Processing, Structure and Properties of Block Copolymers.* Elsevier Applied Science, London and New York.

Goodman, I. (ed.) (1982) *Developments in Block Copolymers 1.* Applied Science, London and New York.

Goodman, I. (ed.) (1985) *Developments in Block Copolymers 2.* Applied Science, London and New York.

Legge, N. R., Holden, G. and Schroeder, H. E. (ed.) (1987) *Thermoplastic Elastomers.* Hanser Publishers, Munich, Vienna and New York.

*Plastics and Rubber Weekly* (1988), October 15, pp. 16–35.

Thorn, A. D. (1980) *Thermoplastic Elastomers,* Rubber and Plastics Research Association, Shawbury, Shrewsbury, England.

Walker, B. M. (ed.) (1979) *Handbook of Thermoplastic Elastomers* (and second edition, 1988). Van Nostrand Reinhold, New York.

Whelan, A. and Lee, K. S. (ed.) (1982). *Developments in Rubber Technology 3.* Applied Science, London and New York.

# 4 Polymer foams

R. G. PEARSON

## 4.1 Introduction

Polymer foam is a term used to describe a system comprised of a gas dispersed in a solid polymer. The gas can be any kind and the polymer may be rigid or flexible. A good example of a foam as a dispersion of a gas in a fluid is the washing water in the kitchen. There can be seen all the requirements to produce a foam, with air dispersed discontinuously by entrainment in the continuous matrix, water. A surfactant helps to stabilise the gas bubbles by reducing surface tension. The shape of the bubbles will initially be spherical but as the volume of gas increases the shape becomes polyhedral as the spherical bubbles impinge on one another. The foam, however, is unstable. With cessation of entrainment of air and further time, the foam decomposes by release of the air. The aim in the production of polymer foams is to consolidate the fluid matrix at the correct moment such that the bubble structure is preserved.

The interest in polymeric foams is in the special properties of these systems. In particular the reduction of density such as to produce materials with values as low as $8\,kg/m^3$ is important. Yet polymer foams with solid surfaces may exhibit quite high stiffness with only a moderate increase in density due to the skin. Compression behaviour is important if the foam is to be used as cushioning or in impact mitigation. Heat transfer properties are of interest if the foams are used for refrigeration or to maintain heat content. These are some of the significant properties of foams which will be looked at later.

Polymer foams are multiphase materials where the disperse phase is usually gas and sometimes may be a liquid. The matrix can be any number of different polymers. Polyurethanes are one of the most common polymer matrices. This is mainly due to the variation in polyurethane properties ranging from rubbery types to give flexible foams to rigid types for the corresponding foam. Many other polymers such as polystyrene and natural rubber are used as matrices in many foams in everyday use.

Various terms are used to describe foams, some of which overlap in meaning. The term cellular plastic is used extensively even when the matrix is rubbery and not plastic. Other expressions are used to imply the foam state, such as *expanded foams* to describe cells of gas in the foam which are strictly discontinuous and generated in a softened solid. Another is *sponge* which implies intercommunicating gas cells (open cell). Flexible foams are arbitrarily those which can give greater than 100% elongation before break. Correspondingly, rigid foams will not. Semi-rigid foams have an intermediate status.

## 4.2 Foam formation and stabilisation

### 4.2.1 Gas generation

Foams are made by introducing a gas into a fluid matrix. There are two classes of gas generation, by inclusion such as mechanical entrainment, or by condensation such as boiling of volatile liquids.

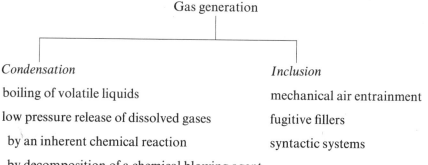

Gas generation

| Condensation | Inclusion |
| --- | --- |
| boiling of volatile liquids | mechanical air entrainment |
| low pressure release of dissolved gases | fugitive fillers |
| by an inherent chemical reaction | syntactic systems |
| by decomposition of a chemical blowing agent | |

Entrainment of gas can be accomplished by driving the gas through orifices mounted in contact with the fluid matrix. The size of the bubbles detached from the orifice is determined by a number of factors described by Rayleigh's empirical relationship

$$V = \gamma r(0.38/\rho_0 g) \tag{4.1}$$

and by

$$V \propto \eta \tag{4.2}$$

where $\eta$ is the viscosity of the matrix, $\gamma$ is the surface tension of the matrix, $r$ is the radius of the orifice, $\rho_0$ is the density of the matrix, $g$ is acceleration due to gravity and $V$ is the volume of the bubble. In general the aim is to produce small volume bubbles.

Fugitive fillers can be compounded into a matrix and subsequently removed and replaced by a gas. Water soluble fillers such as salt or sugar can be incorporated and then leached out by water. Using such fillers in low density polyethylene and polyvinyl chloride gives an open cell type foam.

Syntactic foams are produced by stirring preformed bubbles into the matrix. These may be in the form of single glass balloons of micrometre sizes or agglomerates. Commonly used in epoxy resins, there is an obvious limit to reduction of density because the bubbles are undeformable.

The boiling of volatile liquids which have been incorporated into the matrix is a common method in the production of rigid polyurethane foams. Currently, the liquids used are mostly chlorofluorinated carbons (CFC). A polyurethane foam by this method is likely to be formed by the use of R11, fluorotrichloromethane. This chemical has a boiling point of 24°C (1 bar) and is volatilised by an exothermic reaction in the matrix. Other CFCs are used for special purposes such as foaming at low temperatures, e.g. R12, dichlorodifluoromethane. Current awareness of the detriment to the ozone layer caused by these compounds is leading to change. Other compounds of the same type, such as R123, have been suggested since they are likely to degrade with prolonged exposure to air. Alterations to the type of blowing agent in this technique will certainly lead to changes in the composition of foam formulations. A different example of this type of blowing is in the use of pentanes for polystyrene foams. In this case external heat is used to cause foaming.

Low pressure release of dissolved gases is a similar process in which bubbles are formed by a sudden reduction in pressure to induce boiling.

Gas generation by an inherent chemical reaction is used in polyurethane foam formation. The gas generated is carbon dioxide from the reaction of isocyanate groups which are also involved in the formation of the matrix

$$—R—NCO + H_2O \longrightarrow —RNH_2 + CO_2 \quad \text{blowing}$$

$$—R—NCO + —R'OH \longrightarrow \underset{\text{urethane}}{—RNHCOOR'—}$$

$$—R—NCO + —R'NH_2 \longrightarrow \underset{\text{urea}}{—RNHCONHR'—}$$

matrix formation

Chemical compounds that are not part of the matrix formation reactions can be used. These are termed, chemical blowing agents, of which azobisformamide is a suitable example. It degrades on heating as shown

$$H_2NCONNCONH_2 \xrightarrow{\text{195°C}} \left.\begin{array}{l} N_2 \\ + CO_2 \\ + CO \\ + NH_3 \end{array}\right\} \text{blowing gases}$$

$$+ \text{biurea, cyanuric acid}$$

This is widely used in gas generation in plastic foams. The so-called decomposition temperature, which is essentially the temperature at which a reasonable rate of supply of gas is achieved, can be affected by *kickers* (catalysts) and is therefore adaptable to process requirements. Some of the products of the reaction shown above are solid and act as nucleating sites for gas formation. Examination of the relationship (equation (4.3)) of pressure differences across a curved fluid surface will show that an infinite gas pressure is required to form a bubble of infinitesimally small radius

$$\Delta P = 2\gamma/R \qquad (4.3)$$

where $\Delta P$ is the pressure difference across a curved fluid surface, $\gamma$ is the surface tension and $R$ is the radius of the curved surface. Hence nucleation is needed, probably in the form of gas layers on solid surfaces in the matrix, or by cavitation effects caused by process conditions such as turbulent stirring or impingement mixing.

### 4.2.2 Foam growth

Bubbles are formed and, due to further gas generation, begin to grow. In a typical polyurethane foam formation the bubbles are first seen as a cream-like effect. These bubbles are likely to have a distribution of size at any one time and by extension of equation (4.3), the difference in pressure between bubbles can be

$$\Delta P_{12} = 2\gamma(1/R_1 - 1/R_2) \qquad (4.4)$$

where $R_{1,2}$ are the radii and $\Delta P_{12}$ is the difference in pressure. The gas pressure is highest in smaller bubbles and the difference is decreased by lowering the surface tension. Overall, small bubbles tend to disappear and large bubbles become larger. This process coarsens the foam structure and is usually undesirable. Further, the rate of change in bubble size, apart from more gas generation, is affected by other factors such as temperature and the rate of gas permeation of the matrix. As the foam expands, so structural degradation becomes more evident. Drainage in a capillary effect will remove matrix material from bubble structures until the foam collapses.

### 4.2.3 Foam stabilisation

It is obviously desirable that the draining of foam structures in polymeric foams is not allowed to continue to an extent bordering on complete. This prevention is achieved by a rapid increase in matrix viscosity at a suitable extent of foaming to stop further movement.

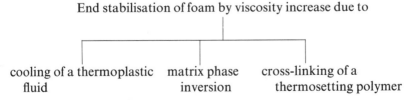

End stabilisation of foam by viscosity increase due to

cooling of a thermoplastic       matrix phase          cross-linking of a
fluid                            inversion             thermosetting polymer

For thermoplastic foams, the gas can be generated in processing equipment such as an extruder, wherein the polymer is heated rendering the melt viscosity low enough to cause flow through the barrel. The blowing gas is

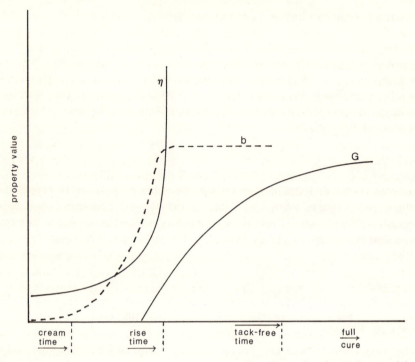

**Figure 4.1** Variation of foam properties with time during foaming: $\eta$, viscosity; $G$, shear modulus; $b$, bubble size.

generated but to a large extent remains dissolved under pressure until the material emerges from the die. Here the gas will generate expansion in the small nucleation bubbles, and the matrix will cool giving an increase in viscosity. It is therefore a matter of balance of the blowing process and the matrix consolidation to provide a satisfactory foam.

Phase inversion may be used to give the required increase in matrix viscosity. A suitable example is that of foaming in a rubber latex. Entrainment of air in the latex can be modelled as discontinuous gas in the continuous phase of an aqueous solution which also contains dispersed rubber. By changing the pH of this matrix, the phases of water and rubber are inverted. This causes an increase in viscosity which fixes the foam. The now continuous rubber phase has the ingredients already added for cross-linking which is activated by heating.

The cross-linking of thermosetting polymers is a chemical reaction that gives rise to rapid increase in viscosity. As shown in Figure 4.1, this increase can be asymptotic. This is possibly accompanied by generation of heat due to exothermic reaction. This in turn gives rise to the blowing action of a volatile liquid. Again the processes must be balanced. If this is not achieved, then unsatisfactory foams are produced. In the case of premature production of gas, the draining process will proceed and the gas will simply boil away. If the consolidation process is too early, then the system will blow when the matrix is well consolidated and then collapse by shrinkage when cooling occurs. This is generally applicable in all the categories.

A description of what may be observed in the production of a polyurethane foam is as previously described, namely the appearance of the gas as bubbles with the appearance of cream. Then the foam rises in the mould. This will continue until the matrix viscosity is too high to allow for further expansion. This is known as *rise time*. However, the matrix is not yet completely cured and will be tacky to the touch, or will form a fibre of material when a spatula is drawn away from the surface. This is an indication that the foam has not yet reached its *green strength* and cannot be de-moulded without distortion. When the surface becomes tack-free de-moulding can be carried out. However, the full cure may not yet be achieved and further time is necessary, possibly accompanied by heating (Figure 4.1).

The controlling feature of foam rise is the asymptotic viscosity rise. The shear modulus increase can be easily demonstrated for an open foaming of a polyurethane and is also implied for other methods of matrix consolidation.

## 4.3 Cell structure

The purpose of this and the next section is to give a description of the cell and total foam structures. Because spherically shaped cells give a minimum interfacial surface area for a given volume, it is fundamental to the shaping of bubbles and can be seen in foams with a relatively small volume fraction of gas. The minimum surface area of spherical bubbles requires the least increase in free energy in their formation

$$\Delta G = 4\pi R^2 \gamma \tag{4.5}$$

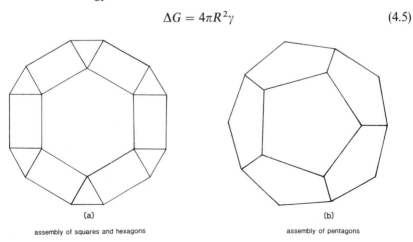

(a)

assembly of squares and hexagons

(b)

assembly of pentagons

**Figure 4.2** Polyhedral bubble shapes: (*a*) assembly of squares and hexagons; (*b*) assembly of pentagons.

where $\Delta G$ is free energy, $R$ is the radius of the bubble and $\gamma$ is the interface surface tension. This relationship indicates that larger bubbles and irregular surface production require larger free energy changes and that reduction in surface tension helps. The maximum packing fraction that single size bubbles with hexagonal packing can achieve is 0.74. When excess of this volume fraction of gas is reached in foam formation, the bubbles adopt polyhedral shapes. The most promising candidates are tetrakaidecahedron (Figure 4.2(a)) and pentagonal dodecahedron (Figure 4.2(b)). The former is more efficient in accommodating the volume fraction, having a relative surface area compared to spheres of 1.06. The latter has a relative area of 1.1. However, on examination of the surface angles, the pentagonal dodecahedron has 108° in the pentagonal faces with 120° between the faces. This gives a greater conformity than tetrakaidecahedron with variation between 90° and 120°. The idealised structure of five-sided faces separating two cells will necessarily have, in real space, a thickness of the face and struts at the intersection of three faces with triangular cross-section (Figure 4.2(a)). This presumes a very small radius of curvature at the point of the angles. Remembering that the polymer matrix is fluid at the formation of the cells, the likelihood is that the angles will be smoothed out (Figure 4.2(b)).

The relationship describing the pressure difference across a fluid curved surface was shown in equation (4.3). This causes the radius of curvature at the angles to be as large as is practical. This is known as the draining model (Figure 4.3(b)) and is closest in form to the shapes of cells seen in many low

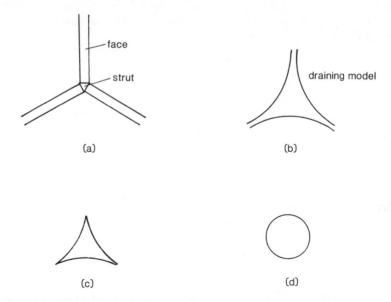

**Figure 4.3** Idealised structures of cell intersections.

density foams. Further degradation of the draining model shape occurs with removal of the faces to give an untenable curved triangular strut (Figure 4.3(c)) which changes to a circular cross-section (Figure 4.3(d)). The minimal struts themselves drain and eventually collapse completely. Drainage due to gravity causes this complete collapse unless the matrix is consolidated. Imperfections in matrix structure such as particulate fillers assist in the collapse. These drainage or imperfection effects may be temporarily healed by mechanisms of matrix flow where surface layer movement repairs serious thinning in the faces of the cell. Two of the mechanisms are known as the Marangoni and the Gibbs effects; they are controlled by the quantity and type of surfactant in the matrix composition. Sooner or later the faces thin beyond repair giving a cell structure which is now interconnecting and is termed an open-celled foam if the matrix is consolidated at this point. As already stated, the fate of an unstabilised foam is complete collapse.

Examination of real foams shows a tendency to the curved shapes with a degree of irregularity which renders attempts to model the structure–property relationships less than satisfactory.

## 4.4 Foam structure

During generation of a foam, the size and shape of the cell structures are changing. When first generated, the gas appears as bubbles with a distribution of sizes. With a condensation process of gas generation, these enlarge further. As has been shown, the significant event in foam stabilisation is the increase in matrix viscosity. Gas may, however, continue to be generated causing elongation of cells as the matrix consolidates. Elongated cells can be shown in a polyurethane foam prepared in an open mould where elongation is in the direction of the foam rise. Such elongation can give rise to ratios of 3:1 in cell axes.

Where the foam comes into contact with the mould, surfaces effects on cell structure can be seen. The foam surface shows a variation of skin textures and levels of collapse with a variety of mould surface types and temperature. This has been used to obtain foams with a significant thickness of solid skin layers giving an increase in stiffness without a significant decrease in foam density. With appropriate material formulations and mould wall temperatures, foams can be prepared with skins typically a few millimetres thick. These are known as structural or integral skin foams. The skin formation occurs by collapse under pressure and leads to density gradient across the foam.

## 4.5 Foam structure–property relationships

### 4.5.1 Introduction

The main uses of foams stem from the physical properties generated by the structure of a solid matrix interspersed by a gas, either as discontinuous or continuous cells. The properties, therefore, depend on the density of the foam as well as the matrix and the cell structure. A particular relation, which will be referred to again later, is that attributed to Egli and Stengard

$$\text{mechanical property} = K\rho_{\text{foam}}{}^n$$

where $\rho_{\text{foam}}$ is the foam density, $K$ is a constant of the system and $n$ is an exponent. Other properties such as heat transfer in insulating foams and mass transfer in cushioning have particular importance.

### 4.5.2 Density

Solid polymers generally have densities around the value of $1000\,\text{kg/m}^3$. The introduction of gas significantly reduces this. If for example a matrix of that density is mixed with a gas of density $1.34\,\text{kg/m}^3$ (air) then a density of $100\,\text{kg/m}^3$ corresponds to a volume fraction of 0.9 of gas. The foams used for thermal insulation often have values in the $30\,\text{kg/m}^3$ region, corresponding to a gas volume fraction of 0.97. For these, there is only a small amount of solid present, which has significant effect on the properties. Generally these are known as *low density foams*. There are other general categories of *high density foams* in the region of $400\,\text{kg/m}^3$ and *microcellular foams* where there is little gas and the density approaches that of the matrix polymer.

### 4.5.3 Heat transfer

One of the most important properties of rigid low density foams, which contributes to a large proportion of polymer foam sales, is that of low heat transfer. These foams are used in refrigeration and freezer plants as well as in preformed board for buildings.

The total heat transfer coefficient is the sum of the individual contributions

$$\lambda_{\text{foam}} = \lambda_g + \lambda_s + \lambda_r + \lambda_c \tag{4.6}$$

where $\lambda$ is the heat transfer coefficient with subscripts g (gas), s (solid), r (radiation) and c (convection). It is generally accepted that the heat transfer by convection of gas in closed cells ($<4\,\text{mm}$ diameter) of low density polyurethane foams is negligible.

Transfer by conductivity through gas is relatively low due to the low mass content of gases. The likely gases in polyurethane foams are fluorotrichloromethane and carbon dioxide giving an approximate value for $\lambda_g$ of $0.008\,\text{W/m/K}$. The particular use of fluorotrichloromethane (R11) is instrumental in producing closed cell structures since it absorbs the exotherm of the matrix forming reaction. It is fairly soluble in the cross-linking fluid but not significantly soluble in the solid matrix. It reputedly diffuses very slowly through the solid polymer and hence is only slowly lost from the product. Additionally, the product foams are mostly clad causing further flow

**Table 4.1** Thermal conductivities of gases

| Gas | Thermal conductivity (W/m/K) |
| --- | --- |
| Carbon dioxide | 0.0148 |
| R11 | 0.0079 |
| R12 dichlorodifluoromethane | 0.0085 |
| Air | 0.0243 |

restrictions. The chlorofluorinated carbons (CFC) group give lowest thermal conductivity (Table 4.1).

Carbon dioxide, the other component gas, has a higher thermal conductivity and is additionally significantly soluble in the solid polymer matrix. It therefore diffuses out of the cells to be replaced by air. This equilibrium is of course faster in unclad panels and is shown in Figure 4.4. Carbon dioxide is frequently used in the blowing of closed cell rigid polyurethane foams for two reasons. Firstly, water is used in the foam production since it produces lower viscosity in the flowing foam, facilitating the filling of a mould. Secondly, the proportion of open cells formed from water-generated blowing allows some dispersion of the heat produced in the formation of the matrix, thus reducing the possibility of localised overheating.

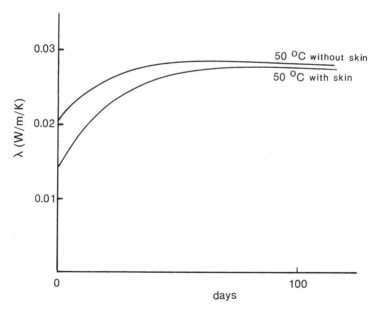

**Figure 4.4** Change in thermal conductivity with time due to gas diffusion with a board measuring $300 \times 300 \times 30$ mm.

Thermal conductivity of the solid matrix is approximately 0.25 W/m/K but consideration of relative volume fraction (0.03 for 30 kg/m$^3$) and orientation of struts gives values between 0.0042 and 0.0023 W/m/K. The former is for heat flow in the direction of the foam rise and therefore in the direction of the strut orientation, the latter for heat flow in the transverse direction.

Radiative heat transfer gives values between 0.004 and 0.006 W/m/K, the lower value corresponding to transfer in the transverse direction to the foam rise. This is due to the greater number of radiation barriers in the form of cell windows in this direction.

The total coefficient value $\lambda_{\text{foam}}$ quoted for a low density polyurethane foam is in the range 0.014–0.018 W/m/K, the lower value corresponding to flow in the transverse direction to the foam rise. Attempts to reduce this value even further are of interest to most refrigerator manufacturers and an expected limit of 0.0125 W/m/K is being pursued. To reduce the matrix component even further will give a lower density and a lower conductivity

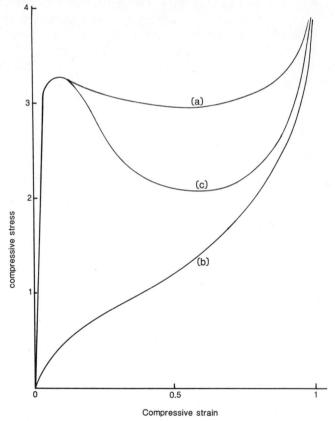

**Figure 4.5** Compressive stress–strain curves for (*a*) rigid foam, (*b*) flexible foam; (*c*) rigid polyurethane foam which does not have a brittle matrix.

but would result in an increase in radiative transfer. An optimum minimum is found around the density value of greatest popularity, $30 \, kg/m^3$.

### 4.5.4 Mechanical properties of foams

It is difficult to encompass all aspects of the mechanical properties of foams. The most important are stiffness in compression and bending, shock mitigation and dynamical mechanical behaviour.

The compression stress–strain curves for some typical polymer foam types is shown in Figure 4.5. The initial modulus gives an indication of whether the foam is rigid or flexible. For rigid foams (a and c), this initial slope may be constant up to a strain in the order of 0.1 and produce a definite compressive strength at a distinct yield point. Flexible foams (b) on the other hand give a continuously varying slope. The behaviour may be modelled as a structure containing rows of columns. At a stress just below that of the compressive strength the columns cease to be compressed linearly and start to buckle. If the columns then fracture, the typical dip in the friable foam curve occurs showing a reduction of stress as the foam collapses. Phenolic foams often show this behaviour (c) due to the brittle nature of the matrix. The other curve (a) for a rigid foam shown in Figure 4.5 is typical of a commercial rigid polyurethane foam that does not have a brittle matrix. Flexible foams are often required for cushioning and stress–strain curves showing a plateau of the kind shown for the rigid foam would feel distinctly uncomfortable. Better response is shown by the flexible foam curve in Figure 4.5 and with relatively low hysteresis. Another assessment of comfort is given by the *sag factor*.

$$\text{factor} = \text{stress at 0.65 strain/stress at 0.25 strain} \tag{4.7}$$

where a value greater than 2.8 is recommended providing the stress at 0.25 strain is suitable for the particular application. Finally, the compressive stress approaches infinity at just below strain $= 1$ as the matrix alone begins to be compressed.

Rusch factorised the observed response of foams to compressive strain. He used a factor to represent the deviation from the initial modulus value as a measure of the various responses

$$\sigma_{cs} = E_f \cdot \varepsilon_{cs} \cdot f(\varepsilon) \tag{4.8}$$

where $\sigma_{cs}$ is the compressive stress, $E_f$ is the initial compressive modulus of the foam, $\varepsilon_{cs}$ is the compressive strain and $f(\varepsilon)$ is the deviation factor. He then correlated $f(\varepsilon)$ with foam performance and constitution and found that it was sensitive to specific details of matrix geometry, moderately dependent on density of the foam and cell size, and independent of variations of the elastic modulus of the polymer matrix. A plot of $\log f(\varepsilon)$ vs. $\log \varepsilon_{cs}$ shows (Figure 4.6) an initial horizontal line for $f(\varepsilon) = 1$ and then a curve which can

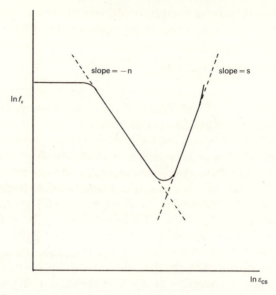

**Figure 4.6** Correlation of foam performance with foam constitution (after Rusch). Typical examples of polyurethane foams are: at test temperature 25°C, $E_f = 0.2$ MPa, $\psi = 0.11$, $n = 0.58$; at test temperature $-196$°C, $E_f = 10$ MPa, $\psi = 0.11$, $n = 1.0$.

be treated piecewise. Thus

$$f(\varepsilon) = m\varepsilon^{-n} + r\varepsilon^{+s} \tag{4.9}$$

Values of the amplitudes and exponents were extensively investigated by Rusch and can be seen in his original papers (1969–1970). For the same rigid foam, the behaviour was examined at temperatures well below any significant transition of the matrix and compared by the factorised relationship. A decrease in $f(\varepsilon)$ and an increase in $\varepsilon$ at the minimum value of $f(\varepsilon)$ indicated an increasing embrittlement of the matrix. Since the qualitative effects of matrix embrittlement is the same for many polymer matrices, it was concluded that $f(\varepsilon)$ is only significantly affected by cell morphology. Rusch also related properties to the density of the foam. He used a function $\psi$ for the volume fraction of the polymer matrix, whereas subsequent investigators have used density ratios and strict correlation requires knowledge of matrix density. A relationship which is significantly affected is the modulus ratio and this can be obtained empirically. It should be compared to the ratio obtained from a modelling procedure shown later

$$\frac{E_f}{E_0} = \frac{\psi(2 + 7\psi + 3\psi^2)}{12} \tag{4.10}$$

where $E_0$ is the modulus of the matrix, and $\psi$ is the volume fraction of the polymer matrix.

Models for the compressive behaviour of foams have been proposed and are based on refined structures such as the pentagonal dodecahedron cell shape with triangular cross-sectional struts. For this, Menges and Knipschild deduced relationships based on the general one of Egli and Stengard. For critical loading of a triangular rod or column, they deduced that

$$\sigma_{cstn} = \alpha a E_0 j 0.0425\,\phi^2 \qquad (4.11)$$

where $\alpha$ is the clamping factor ($= 1$ for rigid and 4 for flexible clamping) usually taken as 2.5, $a$ is the empirical specimen factor, $j$ is the two-dimensional structure orientation factor, $\phi$ is the density ratio, $\rho$(foam)/$\rho$(matrix) and $\sigma_{cstn}$ is the compressive strength. Hence, for the general relationship, the exponent is 2 and from a similar theoretical treatment

exponent $= 1$ for foam tensile strength
exponent $= 2$ for shear strength

For the compressive modulus they deduced a more complex formula

$$\frac{E_f}{E_0} = \frac{C_1\phi^2}{\phi + C_2} \qquad (4.12)$$

where for rigid polyurethane foams $C_1 = 0.65$ and $C_2 = 0.23$, which does not correspond with the relationship proposed by Rusch.

Models developed by Gent and Thomas variously use cubic cells with square cross-sectioned struts and ball intersections for rod struts. For the former model the compressive stress

$$\sigma_{cs} = \frac{E_f f(\varepsilon)' \beta^2}{1 + \beta} \qquad (4.13)$$

where $f(\varepsilon)'$ is a function of the fractional compression of a strut, $\beta = t/l_0$ with $l_0$ the length of the undeformed strut and $t$ the thickness of the strut. Also

$$\frac{E_f}{E_0} \propto \frac{\beta^2}{1 + \beta} \qquad (4.14)$$

For a low density foam, that is with thin struts, $\beta$ is small, and

$$\psi = \frac{3\beta^2 + \beta^3}{(1 + \beta)^3} = 3\beta^2 \qquad (4.15)$$

Substitution gives

$$\sigma_{cs} \propto \psi^2$$

as suggested by the Egli formula.

Foams are used in shock mitigation and vibration damping situations. They can be either flexible or brittle, crushable types. The former are used for multiple impacts and the latter for a single impact. The requirement of the

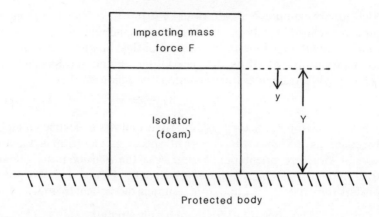

**Figure 4.7** Model of impact mitigating system.

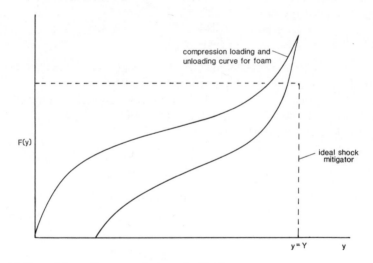

**Figure 4.8** Force-deformation curves for impact mitigation.

foam is that the impacting force is diminished by the isolating foam material. Rusch's correlation of $f(\varepsilon)$ with requirement for shock mitigation showed that the best results were obtained for $n = 1$ and for the largest minimum of $f(\varepsilon)$. This corresponds to a brittle foam with a wide plateau in the compressive stress–strain curve. The area over which the impacting force is extended as well as the thickness of the isolator are also important. The general require-ment for dissipating the energy of the impacting force can also be achieved with a foam exhibiting a large hysteresis. This is a relevant feature in foam mouldings for seats in cars. When the car goes over a bump in the road the driver is vibrated. The extent of the vibration will depend on the type of cushioning.

Foam formulations when processed into a mould or through a die often show some kind of skin, which can be imperfect, containing holes such as may be obtained when water is used for carbon dioxide blown polyurethane foams and it may be very thin. Application artefacts containing foams may have continuous exterior surfaces. For example, rigid polyurethane foams for heat insulation have cladding varying from an aluminium sheet several millimetres thick to aluminium foil mounted on Kraft paper. Semi-rigid foams used in cars for areas such as arm rests may well have vacuum-formed acrylonitrile–butadiene–styrene (ABS) or polyvinyl chloride (PVC) skins to give an acceptable surface. PVC foam formed by the Celuka process has skin induced by post-extrusion flow to pack material at the profile surface. This is an example of an *integral skin* formation whereas the others quoted are sandwich structures. Polyurethane foams can be induced to form solid skins by a combination of techniques. It can be shown that many polyurethane formulations when injected into cooled moulds give skins with an abrupt change in density as the foam core is reached. Such mouldings may give peeling at the surface. The most favoured conditions to give rigid integral skinned polyurethane foams using a specific formulation are to use only a CFC (R11) blowing agent, use a relatively cool (50°–70°C) mould and overpack the material in the mould. The favoured density profile is one with a solid skin several millimetres thick and a foam core with a density variation. Figure 4.9 shows how the mould wall temperature affects the skin thickness for a particular formulation.

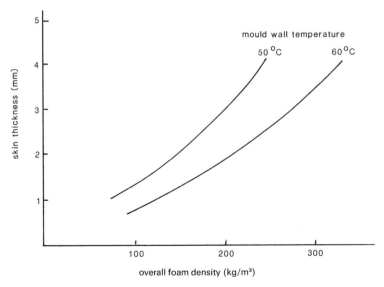

**Figure 4.9** Effect of mould wall temperature on skin thickness of moulding.

The function of the blowing agent R11 (and sometimes methylene chloride), used in integral-skinned polyurethane foams, is to foam the core but become dissolved in the fluid matrix at the relatively cool mould wall, under auto-induced pressure.

Rigid foams with integral skins are called *structural foams* (SF). The combination of a solid rigid exterior with a foamed structure for the core provides a most efficient load-bearing device. An example is bone structure found in nature. Correlation of physical properties with structure is complicated by the density profile from skin to core. Throne has suggested an analytical solution using profile factors (shape factors) substituted to correlate with the observed results. A simplification of this solution is where the solid skin is in contact (non-slip) with a core of constant density. The important property is the stiffness of this kind of structure

$$(EI)_f = S_f = S_o\{(1-e)^3 R'^2 + [1-(1-e)^3]\} \tag{4.16}$$

where $E$ is the modulus of the beam, $I$ the moment of inertia of the beam, $S_f$ the stiffness of the foam beam, $S_o$ the stiffness of the matrix, $R'$ the reduced core density, $\rho_{core}/e_{skin}$ (since $e_0$ is not defined) and $e$ is the reduced skin thickness. This reduces to the Egli relationship

$$S_f = S_o R'^2 \quad \text{when } e = 0 \tag{4.17}$$

The effect of the skin thickness is shown in Figure 4.10 where the relative stiffness of a structural foam with a reduced skin thickness of 0.3 is plotted

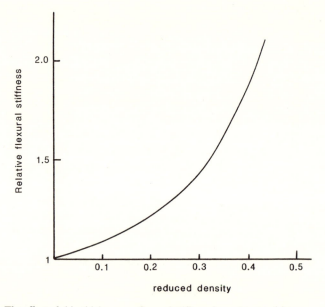

**Figure 4.10** The effect of skin thickness on flexural stiffness for a structural foam.

over a reduced density range. The latter range is limited to less than 0.5 since the core density becomes diminishingly small.

### 4.5.5 Combustibility of foams

Fire is a complex process involving aspects of the physical structure of the materials as well as chemical composition. This has resulted in a large number of testing methods which all aim to give some relation to the way in which materials burn. In many cases the tests aim to simulate real fire situations. Foams are inherently a fire risk since if the matrix is combustible, as most organic material is, a cellular structure gives a large surface area for the spread of flame.

It is not the purpose of this chapter to expound on combustion mechanisms. Essentially this must concern the combustion chemistry of the matrix. Some foams, such as urea-formaldehyde foams, intumesce and are incombustible in normal fires. Others, such as polyurethane foams, can be made less combustible by either cladding or by addition of fire retardants. Cladding may be added to foams for other reasons such as the aluminium cladding for refrigerators and laminating blocks of foam, or non-combustible covering may be used for cushioning. Of the additive fire retardants, phosphorus-containing compounds with halogen-containing compounds appear to be the most effective. Examples of these are dimethyl methyl phosphonate to give a high phosphorus content and bromine-containing polyols as a component of the matrix. The latter by themselves have been shown in some cases to increase combustibility but in conjunction with the phosphorus-containing compound, a synergistic effect has been demonstrated.

Additionally polyurethane type formulations can be varied by having a high isocyanate index, thereby inducing the formation of isocyanurate rings which are inherently more thermally stable than the urethane group. The ring structure is pseudo-aromatic and has built-in stability. These are known as *PIR foams*. As a comparison, a low isocyanate index (105) foam that meets the standard DIN 4102B2 (a combustibility test), requires the inclusion of 4% w/w bromine and 2% w/w phosphorus. Much less is required for a formulation with an isocyanate index of 450 (PIR). (Isocyanate index = (number of mol equivalents of isocyanate/number of mol equivalents of polyols) × 100].

## 4.6 Examples of foam types

To give a comprehensive range of examples would require a much larger work than this, therefore the examples given here are restricted to those showing some variation in foam formulation which has already been discussed. This leads somewhat to an imbalance of information since polyurethanes dominate in terms of variation of types and usage. However, other polymer foams are also quoted.

### 4.6.1 Polyurethane foam (gas generated by inherent chemical reaction or by boiling of a volatile liquid/cross-linking of a thermoset)

The great versatility of polyurethane polymers lies in the ability to produce properties from rubbery to rigid. With foams, this is combined with the ability to range through high to low density and from closed to open cells. These permutations are made possible by varying the formulations.

The formulations consist of two fluids which are mixed to provide the foam. The fluids are essentially immiscible and must be processed through mixing machines. The mixing is achieved either by low pressure, high shear mixing or high pressure liquid impingement mixing. The mixed fluids are then processed into shapes by continuous or discontinuous processing.

High shear mixing machines require the fluid components to be delivered to the mixing head at pressures about $0.3$–$0.4\,MN/m^2$ where they are mixed using a high speed agitator ($> 8000\,rev\,min^{-1}$) designed to give high shear

**Table 4.2** General formulation for polyurethane foam*

| A mixture of | Purpose |
| --- | --- |
| **Fluid A** | |
| (1) Polyol polyether/polyester type (+ filler) (OH number quoted by suppliers) | Polymer formation with isocyanate |
| May also contain 'cross-linkers' and chain extenders | Varies cross-linking density of polymer |
| (2) Water (OH number 6222) | $CO_2$ blowing; promotes flowability in rigid foams; products are incorporated into polymer structure |
| (3) Organic liquid blowing agent R11 (sometimes R12) | Blowing (frothing) |
| (4) Tertiary amines Organometallics (tin compounds) | Catalysts, some with specific activity |
| (5) Silicone/polyether block copolymer | Lowers surface tension, aids mixing, stabilises small bubbles |
| **Fluid B** | |
| Isocyanate, most commonly TDI (RMM, 164; functionality, 2) | For flexible foams |
| MDI (RMM, 250; functionality, 2; impure > 250, $f$, 2.1–2.8) | Impure used for rigids |

Definitions used for balancing formulation quantities:
OH number, number of mg of potassium hydroxide equivalents in 1 g of polyol resin (or water);
RMM, relative molecular mass
$f$, functionality

$$\text{Isocanate index} = \frac{\text{weight}_{\text{isocyanate}} \times f_{\text{iso}}/\text{RMM}_{\text{iso}} \times 100}{\sum \text{weight}_{\text{polyol, water}} \times \text{OH number}/56\,000}.$$

fields. Other facilities required at the mixing head are air and solvent, the first to nucleate bubbles and the latter to flush clean after use.

The high pressure mixing head typically requires the component fluids to impinge on each other at approximately $25 \, MN/m^2$ pressure through 3 mm diameter nozzles. Variations in design for recirculating the fluids is the main difference in the types. For all types, the nozzles dispense the fluids into a chamber in the shape of a cylinder. A piston in the mixing chamber facilitates self-cleaning when the nozzles are shut off. The mixing heads are connected to the feed system comprising storage (bulk) tanks, day tanks, heat exchangers to maintain the component fluids at the correct temperature and metering pumps.

Metering pumps may be categorised into rotary displacement pumps such as gear pumps, or reciprocating piston pumps. Those which operate continuously may be unsuitable for foam formulations that contain any filler, due to mechanical wear. Positive displacement pumps are available for discontinuous ejection into the mixing head, operating rather like injection cylinders and activated by a coupled hydraulic system. The continuously metering pumps can allow mould filling operations such as the manually controlled filling of moulds and continuous slab-stock production.

There are a number of variations in machine design to achieve particular effects. One of these is to reduce the curved upper surface of the foamed block. Designs are also available to produce rod stock.

Moulds mounted on a carousel is an example of a discontinuous moulding process. Otherwise the mould filling may be performed by moving the mixing heads on a counterweight balance from overhead pumping lines to openings in the mould. The moulds may be like those used in the production of thermally insulated doors where aluminium sheeting is stacked in layers to the required spacing and clamped with hand-operated toggle clamps.

Variations in formulations for polyurethane foams give rise to a large number of product types which will differ from one customer to another. Indeed it is the stock-in-trade of industrial formulators. A general formulation for a polyurethane foam is shown in Table 4.2. Subdivision of foam types is shown in Table 4.3.

### 4.6.2 Polystyrene foam (blowing by volatile liquid, cooling of a thermoplastic)

Polystyrene foam as an example of stabilisation by cooling a thermoplastic melt may be blown in a number of ways. The example given here is by volatilisation of a volatile liquid.

Suspension grade polystyrene is produced with about 6% w/w n-pentane (b.p. 36°C) to give a foamable bead. This bead is tumbled in steam to cause the volatilisation of the pentane to about 20-fold expansion of the bead by the formation of small gaseous cells. On cooling, the pentane liquefies and causes a partial lowering of pressure inside the cells. Air permeates in to compensate.

**Table 4.3** Foam types*

| Types | Notable variations in formulation | Notable properties |
|---|---|---|
| Flexible foams | | |
| Polyether type | Using TDI, open cell | |
| Supersoft | | |
| Standard | R11 and water, lower functional polyols, water blowing | Density, 20–40 kg/m³; Compression stress at strain 0.4, 4.5 kPa; Compression set, 2–10% |
| High load bearing | | As above, 6.0 kPa |
| High resilient type | | |
| Super elastic | Primary polyether polyols, modified TDI $f > 2$, no surfactants, post-foaming mechanical crushing | Softer than polyether foams, 2.7 kPa ($\rho_f$ 34 kg/m³) |
| High resilient | Polyethers with organic fillers (SAN) | 6.5 kPa ($\rho_f$, 35 kg/m³); Compression set, 4–15% |
| Polyester type | | |
| Standard | Polyester polyols, tertiary amine catalysts only | $\rho_f$ 60–150 kg/m³; Compression stress at 0.4 strain, 16–90 kPa; Compression set (0.5 strain), 10–30% |
| Semi-rigid foams | Impure MDI, water blown (open cell, primary polyether, R12 (frothing), cross-linkers organotin catalysts | |
| Rigid foams | | |
| Rigids | Impure MDI, R11 (closed cell), small $q$, water flow promoter, polyether polyols | $\rho_f$, 30–45 kg/m³; Compression strength, 0.15–0.3 MPa |
| Integral skin | No water, fillers | $\rho_f$, 600 kg/m³; Flex modulus, 1000 MPa |

* Please note that the data in the table should only be taken as indicative.

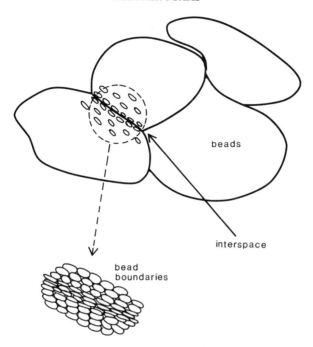

**Figure 4.11** Cell structure in pentane/steam blown polystyrene foams.

The blown beads are then placed into the required mould and again steam-heated. This causes the pentane to revolatilise and the air to expand resulting in a foam with density of about $15\,kg/m^3$.

The structure of the cells is apparent in the product. Certainly bead boundaries are observable. On closer examination the beads are seen as lines of collapsed cells (Figure 4.11). Electron scanning microscopy shows closed cells of 250–750 $\mu$m width and wrinkled walls. It is also apparent that the struts are not particularly well defined. The mechanical strength of the foam is dependent on the production process in that failure usually occurs at the blown beads interface. As with polyurethanes, this foam is an efficient thermal insulator with a value approximately 0.03 W/m/K. This value can be adversely affected by lowering the density to give greater radiative transfer, or by increasing density to give greater matrix conductance.

### 4.6.3 Urea-formaldehyde foam (mechanical inclusion of gas, cross-linking of a thermoset)

Ingredients for the production of the matrix, urea and formaldehyde in aqueous solution, are reacted together to produce a mixture of methylolated ureas as a syrup. When this is mixed with an aqueous solution of an acid such

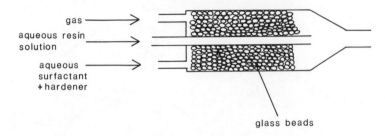

gas

aqueous resin
solution

aqueous
surfactant
+ hardener

glass beads

**Figure 4.12** Gun (schematic) for producing urea-formaldehyde foams.

as phosphoric acid, further reaction will ensue to give cross-linking and a rapid rise in viscosity. Air can be mixed in whilst this reaction proceeds and the product foam stabilises in about 1 min. A surfactant is also usually added. The foam may be produced from a gun (Figure 4.12) where air, surfactant and aqueous acid are passed through packed glass beads to produce a fine foam. The resin syrup meets this flow and mixes in the aqueous solution. Other additives may be included such as polyethylene glycols or thermoplastic emulsions to lessen the effect of subsequent shrinkage due to evaporation of water. This will also cause embrittlement of the matrix which will be lessened by the additives. At first the gas dispersion is almost unicellular. The cell sizes change distribution and the cell membranes (windows) become thin and disrupt due to drying, giving essentially an open cell structure.

The foams are usually brittle and have a compressive strength of about 0.3 MPa. Very low densities are possible. Rigid, home-insulating foams are about 8 kg/m$^3$ and do not support combustion.

### 4.6.4 Chemically blown thermoplastic foam

There are many examples and types of thermoplastic foams formed by thermal decomposition of a blowing agent.

Flexible PVC calendered foams can be formed by heating a formulation of emulsion grade PVC, calcium carbonate filler, a plasticiser such as diallyl phthalate and the blowing agent combination of azobisformamide (about 5% w/w on PVC) and a calcium, barium or zinc salt (about 2% w/w in PVC). This mixture is continuously coated onto a release paper using a doctor blade. This is passed through an oven ranging from 135° to 180°C, followed by removal of the paper backing, embossing and rolling up. This product is a sheet about 2.5 mm thick with a density of about 160 kg/m$^3$.

Rigid PVC foams can be formed as extrusion profiles with skin thickness of 1 mm and a relatively high density core foam. This can be produced by controlled extrusion with a mandrel near the die face to force, under pressure, material to the profile surface and leaving a relatively low pressure behind the mandrel for the core of the extrudate. Further post-die control by a cooled sizing die gives the required surface finish and profile size. Free foaming extrusion can also be used such that as the melt exits from the die, it expands and passes through a cooled sizing die before cooling and cutting.

### 4.6.5 Syntactic foams

These are composed of hollow microballoons held together by a resin. The usual packing fraction of gas is about 0.6 by volume. The system is essentially in three phases; resin, gas and bubble shell. The bubble shell may be that obtained from pulverised fuel ash with gas included. These are cenospheres of mixed metal silicate glasses enclosing carbon dioxide (20–200 μm diameter). The resin is likely to be a curing thermoset, e.g. a cold-curing epoxy resin, which can be treated under vacuum to remove trapped air. This gives a foam of around 500 kg/m$^3$ density. Similarly trapped air in glass microballoons may be used to form foams of the same type.

Compressive stress–strain curves show a typical plateau region at about 70 MPa where the bubble walls collapse. Random arrangement of the balloons occurs providing there is no sedimentation. This indicates that the rule of mixture can be applied

$$E_c = \frac{E_o}{V_o} + \frac{E_s}{V_s} \tag{4.18}$$

and for a hollow sphere

$$E_s = \frac{10E_g}{11 - 5v_g} \frac{t}{R} \tag{4.19}$$

where $E_{o,s,g}$ is Young's modulus of the matrix (o), spheres (s), glass (g), $V_{o,s}$ is the volume fraction, $v_g$ is the Poisson ratio for the glass shell, $R$ is the radius of the balloon and $t$ is the thickness of the glass. For a full study of the deformation of these foams, a more rigorous model should be developed.

The aim in producing syntactic foams is to provide a material with low density and a suitably high compressive shear strength. The most often quoted application is for submersible vehicles and buoys, which must have inherent buoyancy but must withstand large hydrostatic pressures.

## 4.7 Conclusions

The range of blowing systems available allows the formation of a vast number of polymer foams. Those discussed here illustrate some of the properties and methods of production. Further information can be obtained from the suggested literature.

**Further reading**

Meinecke, E. A. and Clark, R. C. (1973) *Mechanical Properties of Polymeric Foams.* Technomics.

Hilyard, N. C. (1982) *Mechanics of Cellular Plastics.* Elsevier Applied Science, Barking.

Oertel, G. (1985) *Polyurethane Handbook.* Hanser.

Gibson, L. J. and Ashby, M. J. (1988) *Cellular Solids—Structure and Properties.* Pergamon Press.

# 5  Long fibre reinforced thermoset composites
R.W. DYSON

## 5.1 Introduction

This chapter is concerned with composites of fibres as a reinforcement for thermoset plastics. The resins used as the polymer matrix are low molecular weight materials which undergo cross-linking to form a three-dimensional network. These materials include polyesters, epoxides, vinyl esters, phenolics and polyurethanes. In each case, the starting materials are in liquid form and during the moulding or shaping process, a high degree of cross-linking brought about by heat or ultra violet light, causes the liquid system to harden to a rigid infusible solid. The thermoset product has reasonable strength and stiffness but relatively poor impact strength; failure is essentially by brittle fracture.

If a high strength, high modulus fibre is incorporated into the liquid system before hardening, the fibre-reinforced product has greatly improved mechanical properties. Glass, carbon and aramid (aromatic polyamide) are the most commonly used fibres. Because the initial resin system is liquid, impregnation of the fibre reinforcement is relatively easy (though not without problems) and the fibre content can be as high as 80%. The fibre can take the form of long or short strands, mattings or woven cloths thereby allowing the resin–fibre composite to be tailored in numerous ways to meet specific requirements.

By suitable choice of hardening agents and conditions, the curing of the resin can be achieved at room temperature or at elevated temperatures. This has led to the development of a wide range of processes for manufacturing products in all shapes and sizes.

**Table 5.1**  Uses of FRP

|                       | %  |
|-----------------------|----|
| Building/construction | 28 |
| Automotive/transport  | 25 |
| Electronic/electrical | 21 |
| Marine                | 12 |
| Sport/leisure         | 7  |
| Consumer goods        | 6  |
| Aerospace             | 1  |

In Western Europe in 1986, about 645 000 tonnes of thermoset fibre-reinforced plastic (FRP) composites were manufactured, mostly glass-reinforced polyester. In 1987, 12 000 tonnes of thermoset FRP were used in advanced composites throughout the world. Table 5.1 shows the relative importance of the various uses of FRP.

## 5.2 The resins

### 5.2.1 Introduction

The principal resins are the unsaturated polyesters, vinyl esters and the epoxides, the latter being used mainly for high performance composites. Other resins include phenolic resols, polyurethanes and polyimides.

Before proceeding to discuss individual resin systems, a few general observations and definitions are made. By selecting appropriate curing agents, thermosetting resins can be hot or cold cured. Curing reactions are exothermic and these can lead to problems, especially with cold curing systems where temperature control is poor or non-existent (e.g. contact moulding). A typical graph of temperature of the resin as a function of time is shown in Figure 5.1. As the temperature rises through the generation of heat, the curing rate increases. The peak in the curve coincides with gelation, which is the formation of insoluble gel material. The time to reach this peak is

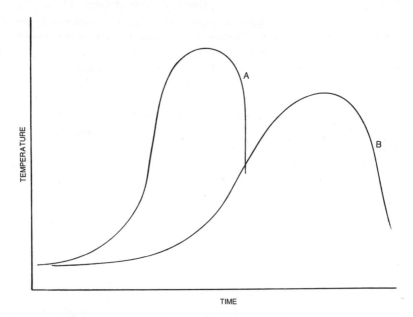

**Figure 5.1** Relation of liquid thermosetting resins (A curing faster than B).

known as the gel-time and is often taken as a measure of the curing characteristics. However, cross-linking is far from complete at this point. The peak temperature is important. Faster cure rates produce shorter gel-times but higher peak temperatures and if the cure is too fast, the peak temperature may exceed the degradation temperature of the resin. This is particularly a problem with thick sections where, because of the poor thermal conductivity of the resins, the centre of the moulding may be considerably hotter than the outside. Even if degradation does not occur, temperature gradients may be severe enough to cause differential contraction on cooling leading to built-in stresses and, in the extreme, to cracking of the moulding. Slow cure and thin sections reduce the risk of thermal problems.

With hot curing, the problems are less because of better temperature control. For example, hot press moulding uses large mass metal moulds and platens which act as a heat sink. Even so, thick sections should be avoided if possible and, where unavoidable, controlled cooling to room temperature should be used. Uncontrolled cooling can result in built-in stresses leading to either warping on cooling or premature failure in service or both. The use of fibres and inorganic powder fillers reduces the problem to some extent, partly because there is less resin per unit volume to cure.

Cure time to the moulder is the time taken from the start of the moulding operation to the time when the moulding has sufficient rigidity to allow demoulding without distortion of the product. This time may be a few minutes for hot moulding to several hours for cold moulding depending on moulding conditions, the curing system and the size of the moulding, especially the thickness. Curing is not complete on demoulding and may continue at room temperature for many months. Even then, there may be residual amounts of low molecular weight material which will act as a plasticiser, for example. For this reason, post-curing is used, especially with high performance composites. Post-curing involves heating at elevated temperatures for several hours after moulding to complete the cure as far as possible and thereby obtain maximum properties. It is particularly advantageous where moulding is at low to medium temperatures.

The terms *pot-life* and *shelf-life* will be encountered. Of necessity, the curing agent is added to a cold curing resin immediately before use. The pot-life is the time between adding the curing agent and when the resin becomes unworkable through cross-linking; it is usually measured in minutes or hours. Shelf-life is usually associated with hot curing systems in which a complete formulation (e.g. a moulding compound or a pre-preg) is prepared and stored until ready for moulding. The shelf-life is the time between formulation and when the material becomes unmouldable; it is usually measured in months. Shelf-life is also applied to resins that become unusable through some instability such as separation on storage or curing even when the curing agent is absent. Shelf-life can be increased by storage at low temperatures (e.g. 0°C, −10°C).

## 5.2.2 Polyesters

These are low molecular weight (1000–2000) resins containing C=C units in the chain to allow cross-linking by the free radical polymerisation of a vinyl monomer, most commonly styrene.

A general purpose resin is made from propylene glycol and a mixture of two di-functional acids. These are maleic acid which provides the unsaturation and phthalic acid which acts as a spacer to control the cross-linking and in particular,

$$CH_3 - CH - CH_2$$
$$\qquad\quad | \qquad |$$
$$\qquad\quad OH \quad\ OH$$

to avoid too high a degree of cross-linking. In practice, in resin manufacture the anhydrides are used rather than the acids. As an alternative to maleic anhydride, fumaric acid

may be used but the resulting polyester is the same because during the polymerisation, the *cis*-form of the maleic inverts to *trans*. The resultant polyester structure may be written

$$\sim\!\!\sim\!\!\sim OOC \diagup \ \ ^\diagdown COO - CH_2 - CH - OOC - CH = CH - COO - CH_2 - CH \!\sim\!\!\sim\!\!\sim$$

and chains have between 10 and 20 ester linkages per chain.

The resins are usually characterised by an *acid value* rather than by molecular weight. The acid value is the number of milligramme equivalents of KOH to neutralise the acidity present in 1 g of resin and is obtained by conventional titrimetry. Acid value decreases with increase in molecular weight and resins are normally produced with acid values in the range 50–20.

When polymerisation has reached the desired stage, the resin is cooled to about 80°C and run off into the vinyl monomer (styrene) which is referred to as the reactive diluent. The final solution contains about 35% styrene. To avoid slow thermal polymerisation on storage at room temperature, small amounts of stabiliser (e.g. 0.05%) are added to give the resin–monomer solution a shelf-life of about 6 months or more if stored at sub-ambient temperatures. Inhibitors used are quinones, hydroquinones and catechols. To avoid photopolymerisation, solutions should be stored in the dark and they are normally supplied in opaque containers for this reason.

These polyester ingredients are used for general purpose resins largely because of availability and low cost. In addition, the resin is compatible with styrene and shows little tendency to crystallise. Resins based on ethylene glycol will crystallise but those based on a mixture of ethylene glycol (80%) and propylene glycol (20%) show little tendency to crystallise and the cured product has improved compression strength compared to propylene glycol-based resins. Other diols are sometimes used but to avoid crystallisation they must not be linear. The most important commercially is butane-1,3-diol.

The properties of the cured resin can also be modified by replacing, wholly or partially, the phthalic acid with other di-acids. Isophthalic acid

gives cured products with improved heat resistance, higher modulus and better resistance to water and alkalis. The use of adipic or sebacic acids produces more flexible cured resins which are used in gel coats for surface layers.

$$HOOC-CH_2-CH_2-CH_2-CH_2-COOH$$
$$HOOC-CH_2-CH_2-CH_2-CH_2-CH_2-CH_2-CH_2-CH_2-COOH$$

Tetrachlorophthalic acid and HET acid impart fire retardancy to the cured resin although the former requires additives such as antimony trioxide to be truly effective.

Styrene is the principal cross-linking monomer because it is readily available and it readily copolymerises with the polyester. The refractive index of styrene cured resins is higher than glass (1.54 and 1.51, respectively) and translucent sheets show the fibre. A mixture of styrene and methyl-methacrylate (80:20) produces a better match of refractive indices and improves the weatherability of the product. Other acrylic esters are sometimes used and di-allyl phthalate is used where the cured product is required to have greater toughness and heat resistance. It is also less volatile than styrene and is therefore useful in formulating pre-impregnated fibre mats. Resin systems based on di-allyl phthalate are always cured at elevated temperatures because of its low reactivity. Styrene based resins continue to be widely used for pre-impregnated mats and moulding compounds.

Curing (cross-linking) is brought about by adding small quantities of a free radical initiator prior to use. These initiators (commonly called catalysts) are usually peroxides or peresters which undergo thermal decomposition although some commercial use is made of the fact that azo-compounds decompose under the influence of ultraviolet light.

All the initiators in common use need elevated temperatures. Lauryl peroxide and di-*t*-butyl perbenzoate, for example, require temperatures of at least 70°C to produce adequate rates of decomposition and hence suitable curing rates. Other peroxides such as di-*t*-butyl peroxide require much higher temperatures and are useful where a long pot-life is required at room temperature and curing at high temperatures is appropriate. Where the initiator is to be mixed by the moulder, it is usually supplied as a paste (e.g. 50% in di-methyl phthalate) to facilitate dispersion in the polyester–styrene solution.

Low temperature (ambient) cure is necessary when, for example, large structures are to be moulded by wet lay-up contact moulding. The two most common initiators are cyclohexane peroxide (CHP) and methyl ethyl ketone peroxide (MEKP). Both are in fact mixtures of peroxides, the composition of which depends on the method of manufacture. MEKP for example has the constituents

$$
\begin{array}{c}
\underset{Et}{\overset{Me}{>}}C\underset{COOH}{\overset{DH}{<}}
\qquad
\underset{Et}{\overset{Me}{>}}C\underset{OH}{\overset{O-O}{<}}\;\underset{Et}{\overset{Me}{>}}C\underset{HO}{\overset{}{<}}Me
\qquad
\underset{Et}{\overset{Me}{>}}C\underset{COOH}{\overset{O-O}{<}}\;\underset{HOOC}{\overset{Me}{>}}C\underset{Et}{\overset{}{<}}
\end{array}
$$

$$
\begin{array}{c}
\underset{Et}{\overset{Me}{>}}C\underset{COOH}{\overset{O-O}{<}}\;\underset{HO}{\overset{Me}{>}}C\underset{Et}{\overset{}{<}}
\qquad
\underset{Et}{\overset{Me}{>}}C\underset{O-O}{\overset{O-O}{<}}\;C\underset{Et}{\overset{Me}{<}}
\end{array}
$$

in various amounts. Consequently the activity of both MEKP and CHP can vary considerably and, notwithstanding this, both require elevated temperatures unless a metal compound is also present. The presence of suitable metal ions allows a redox reaction between the ion and the hydroxide groups to produce free radicals at room temperature at rates acceptable for curing. The most common metal ion is cobalt as Co(II) in the form of cobalt naphthenate or octoate. Other metals are vanadium (as naphthenate), iron (as ferrocene) and tin. The metal compound is generally known as the *accelerator*. Catalyst (peroxide) and accelerator (metal compound) are used in approximately equal amounts. For convenience and safety, resins for ambient curing are usually supplied with accelerator present (pre-accelerated) and only the catalyst need be added. If it is necessary to add both accelerator and catalyst, the accelerator should be added first. The catalyst and accelerator must not be pre-mixed before addition to the resin as this can be extremely dangerous.

As an alternative to the use of catalyst-accelerator systems, room temperature cure can be effected by the use of azo-compounds such as azo-bis-isobutyronitrile (AZDN or AZBN) and ultraviolet light of wavelength around 370 nm. The photo-decomposition of the azo-compounds is independent of temperature but is rate dependent upon the light intensity.

**Table 5.2** Cured resin properties

| | | Ester | Epoxide | Phenolic | Imide | Vinyl ester |
|---|---|---|---|---|---|---|
| Density | g/cm³ | 1.1 – 1.46 | 1.11 – 1.4 | 1.24 – 1.32 | 1.36 – 1.43 | 1.04 – 1.22 |
| Tensile strength | MPa | 40 – 90 | 30 – 90 | 35 – 65 | 75 – 120 | 70 – 80 |
| Elongation | % | 1.5 – 2.5 | 5 – 10 | 1.5 – 2.0 | 8 – 10 | 2 – 5 |
| Tensile modulus | GPa | 2.0 – 4.5 | 1.4 – 4.1 | 2.8 – 4.9 | 2.1 | — |
| Flexural strength | MPa | 60 – 150 | 770 – 140 | 75 – 120 | 135 – 200 | 90 – 125 |
| Compressive strength | MPa | 90 – 250 | 100 – 200 | 85 – 105 | 210 – 280 | — |
| Izod impact | J/12.7 mm | 0.13 – 0.27 | 0.13 – 0.4 | 0.16 – 0.27 | 1.0 | — |
| Rockwell hardness | | | 80 – 110M | 93 – 120M | 52 – 99E | — |
| HDT (1.84 MPa) | °C | 60 – 200 | 50 – 290 | 75 – 80 | 275 – 360 | 100 – 150 |
| Expansion × 10⁵ | mm/mm/K | 5.5 – 10 | 4.5 – 9 | 6 – 7 | 4.5 – 5.5 | — |
| Water absorption | % | 0.15 – 0.6 | 0.08 – 0.15 | 0.1 – 0.36 | ~0.25 | — |
| Shrinkage on cure | % | 4 – 8 | 1 – 4 | — | — | — |

Thermal decomposition of azo-compounds requires elevated temperatures to produce acceptable curing rates.

The amount of peroxide used is usually in the range 0.5–2.0%. The rate of cure is dependent on the amount of peroxide, the rate being approximately proportional to the square root of the peroxide concentration. If too little peroxide is used, the resin system may never harden. If too much is used, problems may arise due to the exothermic nature of the styrene polymerisation. Degradation of polyester resins becomes significant at about 180°C.

The initial resin–styrene mixture viscosity depends primarily upon the molecular weight of the polyester and the concentration used, but usually has values in the region of 3–5 P. It is therefore reasonably fluid. Curing is accompanied by shrinkage which is in the region of 7–9% for unfilled resins.

The properties of the cured resin depend on the type of polyester used as indicated above. Table 5.2 gives an indication of the range of properties of unfilled styrene cured polyester resins. Cured resins can be produced which are hard and rigid or which are soft and flexible, even to the point of being rubber-like. Softening points (BS2782 Method 1029) as high as 200°C can be achieved and impact resistances considerably higher than those shown can be obtained.

Chemical resistance of the cured resins is generally good except in the most hostile environments. However, the presence of ester links renders the cross-linked structure susceptible to hydrolytic attack, especially at elevated temperatures and in alkaline conditions. Suitable choice of polyester and curing system can improve resistance to water.

Electrical properties of the cured resins depend on the number of ester links in the system and on the water absorption. In general, the polar nature of the carbonyl group and water produces lower resistivity and higher dielectric properties than, for example, polyethylene. This limits their use in applications involving high voltage and high frequency insulation.

Polyester resins are the most widely used thermosetting resins in long fibre composites. Over 60% of such composites used in Europe in 1986 were based on polyesters, the usual reinforcement being glass. Despite their limited heat and chemical resistance, they are more than adequate for all but the most stringent of performance requirements and are used in all the areas listed in Table 5.1 including some high performance applications. They are amenable to all forms of processing and their cost is low.

### 5.2.3 Epoxide resins

Epoxide resins are generally made from epichlorhydrin

$$H_2C \underset{O}{\overset{}{\diagdown\diagup}} CH - CH_2 - Cl$$

and bis-phenol A

A step growth polymerisation with the elimination of HCl produces a polymer chain with the general formula

The colour of the epoxide resin depends upon the purity of the bis-phenol A used. If it is impure, the resin is amber in colour, otherwise it can be produced colourless.

The molecular weights of commercial epoxides vary from 340 to 4000 which corresponds to values of $n = 0$ to $n = 12$. When $n = 0$, the product is the di-glycidyl ether. The molecular weight is controlled by the ratio of the reactive ingredients and reaction conditions. In practice, a range of molecular weights is produced.

Resins of average molecular weight less than about 400 are viscous liquids with viscosities in the range 40–300 P at room temperature. Resins with molecular weights above 450 are solids with melting points ranging from 40° to 150°C.

The epoxide resins are usually characterised by their epoxide equivalent rather than molecular weight. Epoxide equivalent is the weight of resin (g) containing 1 g equivalent of epoxy groups and is determined titrimetrically. Epoxide equivalent increases with molecular weight and values for commercial resins range from about 170 (di-glycidyl ether) to about 4000. An alternative assessment is the hydroxyl number defined as the weight of resin (g) containing 1 g equivalent of hydroxy groups.

The epoxide resins based on bis-phenol A and epichlorhydrin are the most widely used generally. Being of low molecular weight, they, like the polyesters require to be cross-linked to make them into useful products. Cross-linking is achieved using amines or acid anhydrides which variously make use of the epoxide end groups or the hydroxy groups along the chains.

In order to achieve higher operating temperatures for the cured resins, various alternatives to the bis-phenol A–epichlorhydrin have been used. Epoxidised novolac resins have received a great deal of commercial attention and these are of the type

Typically $n = 1.5$, giving an average molecular weight of about 650 and an epoxide equivalent of about 180. The resins are extremely viscous (190 000 P) at 25°C but become more mobile at 100°C (5–10 P). They are often used in solution (e.g. MEK) to allow mixing of curing agents or other additives. They are also used with low molecular weight bis-phenol A based resins, usually the di-glycidyl ether. Epoxide systems involving the use of epoxidised resins have higher softening points than those based upon bis-phenol A.

As an alternative to bis-phenol A, bis-phenol F, glycerol and penta-erythritol have been used, among others, in commercial resins

In general these have lower softening points than bis-phenol A resins but those based on glycerol and pentaerythritol can be water soluble. These are sometimes used in conjunction with bis-phenol A resins to improve handling during the mixing of the curing agents or during moulding.

A number of other materials are used for epoxide resins designed specifically for high performance use in composites. The most important of these is diphenylaminomethane which produces tetraglycidyldiamino-methane ((TGDDM) units

Curing of the epoxide chains is brought about by the addition of agents which are generally known as hardeners. The cross-linking chemistry is often very complex but the following outline should provide a useful guide. Cross-linking takes place by means of the epoxide and hydroxyl groups. The latter may be those in the polymer chain or those produced during the curing process by the opening of the epoxide ring. Hardeners may be categorised as follows:

Primary or secondary polyfunctional amines
   and amides                          $H_2N\!-\!R\!-\!NH_2$
Acids or acid anhydrides         $HOOC\!-\!R\!-\!COOH$
Tertiary amines                    $R_3N$

The first react in such a way as to act as bridging agents joining the epoxide chains together and, hence, are polyfunctional. The amount of hardener is mixed in approximately stoichiometric amounts with the resin. Tertiary amines react catalytically and are used in much smaller than stoichiometric amounts.

A great many hardeners within the above categories have been investigated and many are in commercial use. In selecting a hardener for a particular use, the following points are taken into consideration:

(a) Temperature of the cure
(b) Compatibility of the hardener with the resin
(c) Pot-life of the hardener–resin system once mixed
(d) Volatility of the hardener
(e) Physical and chemical properties of the cured resin
(f) Cost.

The following briefly considers the general characteristics of the different categories of hardeners.

Linear polyamines (primary and secondary) are generally low cost and low viscosity hardeners. They are reactive enough to be suitable for room temperature curing but have short pot-lives (up to 2 h depending on batch size). Modified aliphatic amines are available as room temperature hardeners but with improved characteristics such as longer pot-life or faster cure. Examples include amine-ethylene oxide adducts, amine-acrylonitrile adducts and amine-resin adducts. Also in use are polyamides derived from vegetable oil fatty acids such as linoleic acid. Dimerisation or trimerisation of the acid is followed by amination with a polyamine. They were first introduced under the trade name Versamid™ and have come to be known as Versamid curing agents. They are generally less reactive than the polyamines and are usually used for medium temperature curing (50°–100°C). More importantly, the cured resin is tougher, more flexible and with a lower softening point (40°–60°C) due to the flexible chain structure of the polyamides. Aromatic amines have much lower activity than the aliphatic amines and are therefore used for high temperature curing (usually about 150°C). The cured product has better strength and chemical resistance compared with resins cured by aliphatic amines. A general problem with amines is that they are prone to cause dermatological problems.

Acid anhydrides are preferred to the acid because they are more soluble in the epoxide resin and release less water during cure. Compared with the linear polyamines, they have lower viscosity, volatility and reactivity. They are therefore useful as high temperature curing agents (100°–220°C). They can be catalysed to greater reactivity by using organic bases such as tertiary amines. Shrinkage during hot cure is less than with amine hardeners and the heat evolved is less. Cured products have similar properties to those cured by polyamines although selected anhydrides can produce outstanding properties, for example, pyromellitic anhydride produces cured products with very high softening temperatures.

Tertiary amines operate catalytically and are used either as the sole curing agent or as the co-curing agent with polyamines and polyamides, or as accelerators for anhydride curing agents. When used alone, tertiary amines often have very long pot-lives and require high temperature curing and, usually, post-curing.

The viscosity of liquid resins may be too high for some applications including the impregnation of fibre mats. The viscosity can be reduced by the use of diluents which also make mixing with the hardener easier. Diluents may be non-reactive (e.g. xylene, toluene) or reactive (e.g. low molecular weight mono- or di-epoxide compounds, tri-phenyl phosphite, $\gamma$-butyro-lactone). Reactive diluents are often preferred because they become bound into the system and do not cause problems through volatilisation. However, volatilisation may be a problem in pre-cure stages during handling and forming. The diluents are more volatile than the epoxide resins and since they are used at about 10 pph, processes using vacuum techniques for example, could significantly change the system's composition before the diluent has reacted.

Flexibilisers are sometimes added to the resin to reduce brittleness in the cured resin. These are low molecular weight polymers which become incorporated into the network and provide flexible links in the system. They are polyamides (which are also curing agents), polyanhydrides and poly-sulphides. Whilst flexibilisers impart toughness, it is at the expense of stiffness, strength and heat resistance.

The properties of the cured resin depend, as would be expected, on the type of epoxide used and the extent of cross-linking but, in addition, they are markedly dependent on the curing system used. Table 5.2 shows the general range of properties of the unfilled resins. The rigid resins have mechanical properties that are not very different from polyesters. A significant difference is that much higher heat distortion temperatures (HDTs) can be obtained and some formulations (e.g. those based on epoxidised novalacs) can achieve HDTs approaching 300°C. Other notable differences are that the rigid resins have lower thermal expansion coefficients, shrinkage on cure is less (2–5%) and water absorption is lower.

Electrical properties are somewhat better than polyesters for insulation purposes and chemical resistance is also generally superior. Cured epoxides are resistant to acids and alkalis although acid cured resins are less resistant than amine cured resins. They are only slightly affected by chlorinated hydrocarbons and ketones but otherwise they are solvent resistant.

Despite their superiority over polyesters with regard to heat and chemical resistance, epoxide resins are not as widely used because of their higher cost and greater difficulty of processing. They tend to be used where their superiority makes their use inevitable and where cost is a minor consideration. They are the principal resins for high performance composites and account for about 80% of resins used in this area. The principal reinforcement is carbon fibre with aramid fibres being used where toughness is required.

### 5.2.4  Vinyl ester resins

These resins were developed in the USA where, at present, they are much more widely used than in the UK. The general purpose vinyl esters are made by reacting low molecular weight epoxides with, usually, either acrylic or methacrylic acid to produce a chain structure such as

$$CH_2=\overset{\overset{\displaystyle CH_3}{|}}{C}-COO\left[CH_2-\overset{\overset{\displaystyle OH}{|}}{CH}-CH_2-O-\bigcirc-\overset{\overset{\displaystyle CH_3}{|}}{\underset{\underset{\displaystyle CH_3}{|}}{C}}-\bigcirc-O\right]_n CH_2-\overset{\overset{\displaystyle OH}{|}}{CH}-CH_2-OOC-\overset{\overset{\displaystyle CH_3}{|}}{C}=CH_2$$

Such polymers therefore have the characteristics of epoxide resins but can be cured by using the vinyl monomers used with polyesters. Because the C=C involved in cross-linking is terminal, curing of vinyl esters is more rapid than with the polyesters under the same conditions. The styrene or other monomer is usually used in somewhat greater amounts than with the polyesters (35–50%).

The cured resins are generally tougher than the polyester resins because of the epoxide structure and chemical resistance is also better. In particular, the hydrolysis resistance is much improved by virtue of the fact that there are fewer ester linkages and those that there are, are shielded by the cross-link. Because of their epoxide nature, the resins have better wetting characteristics than the polyesters. In short, these resins show the virtues of epoxides with the advantages of polyesters with regard to processability.

Various modifications to the resins are commercially available. The use of halogenated resins improves fire resistance, especially when small amounts of antimony trioxide are incorporated into the system. Rubber modified resins are available with increased toughness at the expense of rigidity. Of particular note are the epoxidised novolac vinyl esters of the type

This structure leads to a higher cross-link density which improves heat resistance in the cured product. Heat distortion temperatures in the range 130°–150°C can be achieved. Heat ageing characteristics are also improved.

## 5.2.5 Phenol formaldehyde resin

These resins have been used as moulding and laminating resins when reinforced with cellulosic fibres for over 70 years. During that time, some use has been made of glass as a reinforcement but in recent years this has assumed

increasing significance, principally because glass-reinforced resins not only
have suitable mechanical properties but inherent fire resistance and low
smoke emission.

Resol resins are used for laminating since they are readily obtained in liquid
form with viscosities in the range 4–360 P. They are made by reacting a
phenol or modified phenol with an excess of formaldehyde (as formalin) or
sometimes furfuraldehyde, under alkaline conditions. This gives a mixture of
polymethylolated phenols such as

as well as mono-methylolated phenols. The relative amounts of these species
depends on the excess of formaldehyde and reaction conditions. The methylolated phenols condense rapidly to form species such as

and further heating eventually leads to cross-linking. These subsequent stages
are relatively slow and the reaction is stopped after the initial fast reaction
when there is a mixture of polymethylolated phenols containing an average of
about two benzene rings. This mixture is the resol. Water is removed by
distillation under reduced pressure after neutralisation to reduce the rate of
further reaction. Neutralisation also has the effect of reducing the colour
intensity of the resol.

Resols are normally used in solution and the choice of base catalyst and
other reaction conditions affects the solubility characteristics of the resin. If
caustic soda is used, the resol is water soluble but if ammonia is used, the resol
is spirit soluble, isopropanol (IPA) being the most widely used solvent. When
water-based resins are produced, the water is only partially removed at the
distillation stage and, typically, the final product will contain about 30%
water.

As mentioned above, resols can be cured by heat alone but the rate is
dependent on pH. Rapid cure occurs in acid or alkaline conditions and is a
minimum at pH 7–8. Neutralised resins are therefore more stable at room
temperature and shelf-lives of 2–6 months are normal. When curing is
required, the current practice is to add strong acids such as *p*-toluene
sulphonic acid or inorganic acids (or both) at levels of 5–12%. Cold curing
takes 1–15 h depending on acid type and concentration and also upon

moulding thickness. Cure times of a few minutes can be achieved at elevated
temperatures (60°–80°C). A serious problem with acid curing is the corrosion
of conventional metal moulds. Development work is in progress to produce
suitable alkaline catalysts.

The curing rate can be controlled by suitably modifying the phenols to
adjust the reactivity of the resols. The *p*-methylol phenols are more reactive
than the *o*-methylol phenols. By blocking either the *o*- or *p*-positions,
methylolated phenols can be made more reactive for fast cure or less reactive
for slow cure. Resins can therefore be tailored for specific curing needs. For
example, wet lay-up resols are usually water based but in any case water is
evolved during cure. A slow cure allows the water to escape from the lay-up
during cure and post-curing at 60°–80°C leads to an improvement in the
ultimate properties of the cured product.

Spirit soluble resins (solids content typically 50–60%) are used principally
for the production of pre-pregs in which fibre is pre-impregnated with the
resin solution after which the solvent is removed. Curing of the pre-preg is at
130°–140°C with cure times in the region of 10–30 min. Pre-preg shelf-life is
usually about a month at room temperatures but can be increased to almost a
year if stored at −10°C.

Some use is made of novolac–resol blends. These have shorter cure times at
130°C and longer shelf-lives than resols alone. Novolacs are made by reacting
an excess of phenol with formaldehyde under acidic conditions to produce
low molecular weight species such as

and they typically contain up to six rings. They are incapable of cross-linking
alone.

Typical properties of a cured resol are shown in Table 5.2 and, as will be
seen, resols have mechanical properties similar to those of polyesters and
epoxides. The principal reason for their use as laminating resins lies in their
burning characteristics. Unlike polyesters and epoxides, they are inherently
fire resistant and produce very little smoke when they do burn. Resins are
available with a limiting oxygen index of 46, with a rating of *not ignitable*
(ASTM D229) and with a surface flame spread of *class 1* (BS 476 pt 7). These
resins are also certified *class 0* under UK Building Regulations E15 and meet
the fire regulation requirements of most countries.

Epoxide and polyesters can be modified either structurally or by additives
to satisfy many fire tests. However, when they do burn, it is with the emission
of considerable amounts of smoke. Phenolic resins burn with minimal smoke

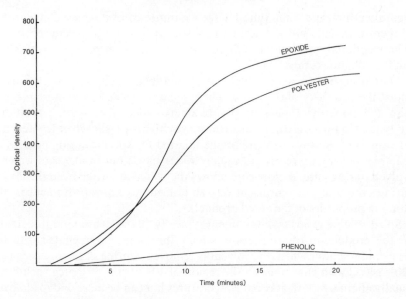

**Figure 5.2** Rate of smoke generation for typical GRP panels in an NBS smoke chamber.

and visibility is about a hundred times that obtained with fire retardant polyester laminates under the same conditions (Figure 5.2). Consequently, phenolic-glass laminates are now preferred to others in applications involving public safety. These areas include transport, hospitals, airports, railway stations and mines.

Phenolic resins are also inherently stable to degradation, corrosion and weathering. Glass-reinforced laminates have a continuous service temperature of 180°–200°C which is considerably better than polyester laminates. Some phenolic laminates can withstand 260°C for a short time.

### 5.2.6 Polyimides

These materials are not in general use but are used for special applications where exceptional heat resistance is required. True polyimides are not the most tractable of materials but several are available as low molecular weight materials which polymerise and cross-link when heated. They are used in the manufacture of carbon or glass pre-pregs for laminating and filament winding. Among the most widely used are those based on bis-maleimide under the name Kerimid™. The structural type is

It is notable that the polymerisation is by an addition and not a condensation mechanism. Another type is Skybond-700™ with structure

It is supplied as a solution of monomeric reactants which cure to the polyimide structure. Some polyimides are acceptable for continuous service at 275°C.

It may be noted here that some thermoplastic polyimides (polyether-imides and polyamide-imides) are also used in forming pre-pregs for high temperature use.

## 5.3 Fibres

### 5.3.1 Introduction

The use of long fibres of greater strength and modulus embedded in a weaker resin matrix can produce a composite of greater strength and stiffness than the resin itself. The improvement depends on the properties of the fibre and the amount used. If a stress is applied to an ideal system in the fibre direction, the stress is shared by the resin and the fibre in proportion to the volume of each. It can be shown that the tensile strength of the ideal composite is given by

$$\sigma_c = \sigma_f \phi_f + (1 - \phi_f) \sigma_r$$

where $\sigma$ is the stress, $\phi$ the volume fraction and the subscripts c, f, r denote composite, fibre and resin, respectively. $\sigma_r$ is not the break stress of the resin but the stress carried by the resin at the strain at which the composite fails. The modulus $(E)$ of the composite is given by

$$E_c = E_f \phi_f + (1 - \phi_f) E_r$$

In the transverse direction, there is no fibre reinforcing effect on strength properties; the stress is the same for all components

$$\sigma_r = \sigma_f = \sigma_c$$

and failure will occur when the ultimate tensile strength of the resin is reached. The transverse modulus is given by

$$E_c = \frac{E_f E_r}{\phi_f E_r + (1 - \phi_f) E_f}.$$

These equations are derived from simple models and have limited use in practice. In particular, the longitudinal stress equation assumes perfect adhesion between fibre and resin. Adhesion is much less than 100% and is usually around 50%, often less. In the extreme case when adhesion is zero, the fibres simply slip through the resin and no stress is transferred to the fibre. Failure is therefore dictated solely by the resin and since there is less resin per unit volume in the composite compared to the unreinforced resin, failure of the composite occurs at a lower stress level than with the resin alone. It is therefore imperative that adhesion should be as high as possible to achieve maximum strength. Adhesion is also significant in other ways. At failure, all of the fibres do not break simultaneously but in sequence at points of weakness as the stress is increased. When a fibre breaks, two ends are produced which will pull away from each other unless adhesion between resin and fibre prevents this. If this is the case, the effect of a broken fibre has less significance than otherwise and the composite is able to withstand the applied stress. If adhesion is low and the broken fibre ends pull away, the remaining fibres carry a greater share of the stress to compensate which ultimately results in the composite failing at a lower applied stress. The fewer fibre ends there are in the composite, the stronger the composite will be. A composite will therefore have greater strength if there are fewer fibre ends in the first place and continuous fibres should produce the highest strength of all.

Another assumption is that the resin matrix is continuous, i.e. there are no voids. This can be difficult to achieve in practice. Impregnation of fibres by liquid resins can be accompanied by air entrapment or by the evolution of volatiles. The voids have greatest significance if they occur at the resin–fibre interface because adhesion is then zero. Voids can be minimised by using high pressure moulding techniques or vacuum impregnation techniques. The latter, as noted above, can lead to other problems such as extracting volatile components from the resin.

### 5.3.2 Glass fibres

Glass is a polymeric silicate in which ionic silicate chains are held together by metal ions

It is made by melting silica ($SiO_2$) with various metal oxides. If the molten glass is extruded through a spinneret and cooled as it is extruded, filaments of

**Table 5.3** Composition of glasses

| Glass | $SiO_2$ | $Al_2O_3/Fe_2O_3$ | CaO/MgO | $B_2O_3$ | $Na_2O$ |
|-------|---------|-------------------|---------|----------|---------|
| E | 52.4 | 14.4 | 21.8 | 10.6 | 0.8 |
| C | 63.6 | 4.0 | 16.6 | 6.7 | 9.1 |
| S | 64 | 26 | 10 | 0 | 0 |

glass fibre are produced. The filament diameter is 9–15 μm. The use of different metal oxides in controlled amounts leads to a range of glasses with different properties. The most commonly used glass for reinforcement is *E-glass*. Other glass compositions used in fibre reinforcement include: *C-glass*, which is a corrosion-resistant glass used in the form of tissue for surface layers of laminates used in corrosive environments such as chemical plant; *S-glass* and *R-glass*, which have higher modulus than E-glass and are used where higher performance composites are required, for example, aerospace applications. Glass compositions are given in Table 5.3 and typical fibre properties are shown in Table 5.4.

Having cooled the fibres, they are passed through a bath containing a complex liquid sizing mixture to coat the glass surface. The size provides a protective layer to reduce mechanical damage to the filament surface during handling. It also improves adhesion of the resin to the glass by increasing wettability and makes the glass chemically reactive towards the resin so that a chemical bond is developed between the two during curing. In the case of glass/polyester systems, pendant C=C groups are attached to the glass

**Table 5.4** Fibre properties

| Fibre | | | Tensile | | Density (g/cm$^3$) |
|-------|---|---|---------|---------|----------|
| | | | Strength (GPa) | Modulus (GPa) | Density (g/cm$^3$) |
| Glass | E | | 3.6 · | 76 | 2.56 |
| | S | | 4.5 | 86 | 2.49 |
| | R | | 4.4 | 85 | 2.58 |
| Carbon | | | | | |
| 1st generation | | HS | 3.55 | 235 | 1.81 |
| | | IM | 3.3 | 300 | 1.8 |
| | | HM | 2.5 | 358 | 1.85 |
| 2nd generation | | HS | 10 | 295 | — |
| | | IM | 5.58 | 294 | 1.8 |
| | | HM | 3.8 | 400 | 1.75 |
| Aramid | | | | | |
| Nomex™ | | | 0.67 | 17.6 | 1.4 |
| Kevlar™ 29 | | | 2.7 | 60 | 1.44 |
| Kevlar™ 49 | | | 3.0 | 134 | 1.45 |

whereas for glass/epoxide systems, the group is —NH or —OH. In practice, glass is usually made with groups suitable for polyester or epoxide resins. The coupling agents are usually silanes such as vinyl trichlorosilane or γ-amino-propyltriethoxysilane

$$CH_2{=}CH{-}SiCl_3 \qquad NH_2{-}(CH_2)_3{-}Si{-}(OCH_2CH_3)$$

with allyl trichlorosilane resorcinol as a typical dual function coupling agent

In all cases, the silane couples to the glass surface by reacting with the hydroxyl groups on the glass surface. Other types of coupling agent are also in use (see Chapter 1).

Adhesion promoters include fatty acids (stearic acid, salicylic acid) and amines (especially piperidine derivatives).

### 5.3.3 Carbon fibres

Carbon fibres are made by suitable heat treatment of polyacrylonitrile (PAN) fibres although other fibres such as cellulose have been used. The PAN filaments, around 10 000 at a time, are first oxidised in air at 200°–250°C. The filaments are then tensioned to maintain polymer chain alignment in the fibre-axis orientation. They are then *carbonised* at 1000°–1500°C under tension in the absence of oxygen. At the end of this stage, the filaments are essentially micro-crystalline carbon and porous due to escaping volatiles. The final stage, *graphitisation*, involves heating at temperatures up to 2800°C in the absence of oxygen during which the structure becomes essentially that of graphite. Because of the problems of weaving graphitised fibre, it is usual to weave the oxidised fibre and then carbonise and graphitise the woven cloth. In many cases, carbonisation of the cloth gives adequate properties.

Fibre strength is developed during carbonisation and modulus during graphitisation. This has led to two fibre types; high modulus (HM) which is also known as type I and high strength (HS), also known as type II. By suitably controlling the temperatures during carbonisation and graphitisation, the modulus and strengths can be controlled giving rise to fibres with intermediate strength and modulus. These are known as IM fibres.

The first fibres produced by the above process were based on acrylic fibres for textile use. These fibres are not pure PAN but copolymers, containing about 10% of a comonomer to facilitate dyeing. The carbon fibre produced from these is therefore imperfect compared with fibres produced from PAN. The use of better precursors and pre-oxidation stretching to increase chain orientation has led to improvements in both strength and modulus (Table 5.4). Other modifications to the basic process have led to fibres with reduced diameter (from 8 to 5 μm) and an increase in breaking strain from 1.2% to around 2%.

The fibres are usually sized to improve adhesion between resin and fibre. Treatments include the use of sodium hypochlorite and various acids (sulphuric, nitric, acetic) to clean and etch the fibre surface followed by appropriate coatings such as liquid epoxides.

### 5.3.4 Aramid fibres

These are aromatic polyamides of which two are widely known by their Du Pont trade names; Kevlar™ and Nomex™. Their structures are

Kevlar                                          Nomex

These polymers are both crystalline but the melting points are too high for them to be melt spun into fibres. They are therefore spun from solution. Kevlar fibres have greater crystallinity due to the more symmetrical molecular structure and the crystallinity is further enhanced by the liquid crystalline nature of the polymer solution. Kevlar fibres consequently have higher strength and modulus than Nomex fibres and are therefore preferred for reinforcement. However, Nomex fibres are used to produce Nomex 'paper' by a process similar to conventional paper making. It has exceptional stiffness and is made into Nomex honeycomb which is used as a light-weight stiffening layer bonded between outer layers of FRP in the production of high performance structures, e.g. boats, aircraft. The Nomex paper binding agent is either a phenolic or an acrylic modified epoxide resin which does not fully cure until the final stages of construction to allow the honeycomb to remain flexible during lamination and to improve bonding to the outer skins. The important properties of the fibres are shown in Table 5.4.

Table 5.4 shows that carbon fibres have the highest modulus and are therefore best suited as stiffening agents in composites. Carbon fibre is, however, expensive and its use is principally where high modulus and/or heat resistance are required despite the cost. Glass fibres are the cheapest of the fibres and are therefore the most widely used despite their lower modulus and greater density. The Kevlar fibres are intermediate between glass and carbon fibres with respect to both modulus and price. They have the advantages of low density and greater toughness with the ability to suffer large strains without failure. Kevlar fibres have lower heat stability compared with glass or carbon but since the recommended maximum service temperature is around 400°C this is not a serious disadvantage. The three major types of fibre are often used in combination to achieve the appropriate blend of properties in a cost effective manner.

Some use is made of other fibres such as boron fibres which have a modulus greater than 400 GPa but their use is very limited due to the high cost of production. New developments with commercial potential are ceramic fibres which can be woven and are capable of withstanding 1000°C. High modulus polyethylene fibres also have potential but are limited to a maximum temperature of a little over 100°C and the fact that they will creep under load, although cross-linking could solve this problem.

More conventional fibres such as cotton and other cellulosics, nylons and polyesters are occasionally used but lack the strength and stiffness of Kevlar which also has better heat resistance. Despite its high cost, Kevlar has become the most used synthetic organic fibre.

### 5.3.5  Fibre formats

Fibres spun from melt or solution are produced as continuous *filament* of diameter in the range 5–15 μm. The filaments are collected in bundles of about 100 to form continuous *strands*. Several strands combined together form continuous *roving*. If the roving is twisted to lock the strands together, it is called *yarn*. Continuous roving is used to produce uni-directional reinforcement but is also used (usually as pre-preg) in layers at various angles to produce reinforcement in different planar directions. It is also used in filament winding and pultrusions.

Yarn and roving can be woven in various ways to form *cloth*. Weaving reduces interlaminar failure in the final product and produces bi-axial reinforcement since the fibres are at right angles to each other. However, the crimp in the fibre at the points of intersection reduces the reinforcement efficiency which is at a maximum when the fibre is straight. Three types of weave are common; plain weave (over and under), twill (over and under every other fibre) and satin in various forms, all of which involve a fibre passing over or under more than two fibres (e.g. four, eight). Because there is less crimp in satin weaves, they give the best reinforcement and are preferred for high performance composites. Three-dimensional fabrics can be obtained by stitching layers of cloth together with polyester or aramid threads.

Non-woven fabrics are made by either knitting or by stitching continuous rovings together. In the latter case, reinforcement in the stitched direction is less than when woven, but stitching avoids the problems of crimp. It allows for easy handling of the rovings in sheet form and helps to reduce interlaminar shear. By layering the rovings in different directions before stitching, strength can be obtained in preferred orientations. Three-dimensional reinforcement can be obtained by stitching layers of non-woven cloth together.

Continuous strands which are loosely stitched together, principally for ease of handling, are known as *needle mat*. *Chopped strands* are made by chopping continuous strand into short fibre lengths (3–100 mm) and are used in formulating *dough moulding compounds* (DMC) and in forming *chopped strand mat* (CSM) which is convenient to handle. CSM is made by spraying the strands together with a binder onto a rotating drum where they form a randomly orientated fibre mat. They are available in different weights (amount of glass per unit area) and are widely used because of the ease of resin impregnation and low cost in processes such as hand lay-up and resin injection. CSMs are relatively inefficient at reinforcement because of the short fibre lengths. Better reinforcement can be obtained by using continuous strands which are swirled into place to form a mat, known either as *continuous strand mat* or *swirl mat*. The principal reason for using continuous strand mat, however, is that it can be stretched more than CSM without breaking and can therefore be pre-formed with a deeper draw than CSM. It is most commonly used in compression and resin transfer moulding.

*Glass tissue* is a fine chopped strand matting of about 0.3 mm thickness for

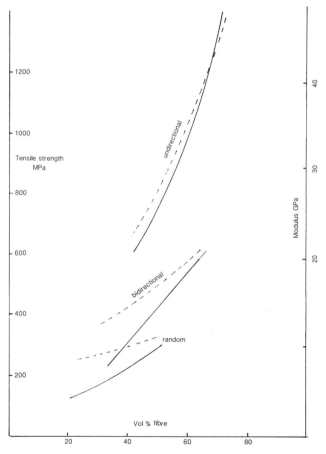

**Figure 5.3** The effect of glass fibre on tensile modulus and strength of polyester resins: ----, modulus; ————, strength.

use in surface layers. It takes two forms, *surface mat* with about 12% binder and *overlay mat* with about 1% binder. The former is designed for use in hand lay-up and other contact moulding processes whilst the latter is for use in closed moulding processes. Both are designed to give good resin wet out and hence produce a good surface finish to the product.

The degree of reinforcement and type of reinforcement depends upon the fibre format and the amount of fibre used. Figure 5.3 gives an indication of the reinforcement obtained when different formats of glass fibre are used with a polyester resin. It also indicates the typical levels of fibre loading for each type.

Fibre combinations are used for some high performance composites. For example, cloth can be woven from a mixture of carbon and Kevlar, the carbon to provide strength and stiffness and the Kevlar to provide toughness and impact resistance in the composite. Alternatively cloths of different fibres can be used in layers set at angles if necessary. A large number of possible combinations allows the designer to optimise property requirements in the final product.

## 5.4 Additives

Various components may be present in addition to the resin, curing agent and fibre to modify or control properties. Inorganic powder fillers such as chalks and clays are used to control shrinkage on curing. They are an essential ingredient of DMCs and sheet moulding compounds (SMCs) where they produce appropriate handling characteristics as well as controlling shrinkage. Powder fillers also improve machinability and reduce thermal expansion. Surface treated fillers allow the use of finer particle sizes with better dispersion in the resin (see Chapter 1).

Alumina trihydrate (ATH) is used as a fire retardant but since it is used in large quantities, it also acts as a bulking filler like chalk and clay. As a fire retardant, it decomposes endothermically at about 200°C to produce water. Whilst the temperature of 200°C is a limiting factor for use with thermoplastics, the material is well suited to thermosets which cure at much lower temperatures. Another common fire retardant is antimony trioxide at loadings of a few percent. It is used in conjunction with halogenated resins or with halogen-containing additives. The latter are often halogenated waxes in which case mechanical properties can be downgraded. Low viscosity resins such as polyesters may have thixotropic agents added if they are intended for hand lay-up use on vertical surfaces. The principal thixotropes in use are silica aerogels at about 2% loading. SMCs also contain thickening agents so that once the sheet is formulated, the resin thickens to form an almost tack-free sheet for ease of handling. These thickening agents are also known as livering agents. Polyester SMCs contain metal salts such as MgO which react with the acid end groups of the polymer. These can also be used with vinyl ester SMCs but if isocyanates are used, more rapid thickening occurs through reaction with hydroxyl groups.

The presence of rubbers produces a tougher composite with greater impact resistance. However, the rubber also reduces the stiffness and heat resistance of the composite by an amount dependent on the quantity of rubber added. A recent development involving the use of a surface modified silicone rubber dispersed in the resin is claimed to produce improved impact resistance with little or no loss in other properties at loadings up to 20%. Furthermore, toughness is maintained down to $-50°C$. The surface treatment of the silicone depends on the resin to be used but treatments are available for the resins described in section 5.2 above.

Other additives include colouring agents, light stabilisers and internal mould release agents.

## 5.5 Fabrication methods

Composites can be fabricated as sheets, rods and tubes or as moulded shapes using a wide variety of processes with any of the above fibres (singly or in combination) and resins. In practice, some fibre/resin/processing combinations are more widely used than others.

### 5.5.1 Wet lay-up

Wet lay-up processes involve liquid resins applied manually and cured at or a little above room temperatures at low pressures and with relatively simple tooling.

*Contact moulding* is a process whereby a simple mould shape is coated with layers of fibre and resin to the required thickness. The resin can be applied by hand (*hand lay-up*) or by spray gun (*spray lay-up*). In the former method, the resin is applied by brush or roller to the fibre in the form of matting, usually chopped strand mat. In spray lay-up, the resin is sprayed onto the mat which is applied by hand or both the resin and the fibre are sprayed, in which case a twin-barrelled gun is fed with continuous roving which is chopped in the gun and discharged from one barrel into the resin which is sprayed from the other barrel. Whichever method is used, the following sequence is followed: the mould is coated with release agent and a gel coat is applied to a thickness of 0.25–0.4 mm. The gel coat is a resin-rich formulation containing pigments and mineral filler if required. It is important to produce an even thickness of gel coat to obtain even cure and to ensure a good and durable surface finish. When the gel coat is touch dry, a layer of the main laminating resin is applied followed by the fibre mat. A further layer of resin is applied and this is stippled or rolled to impregnate the fibre mat with resin and to ensure that as much air as possible is removed. Further layers of matting and resin are applied with stippling or rolling of each layer until the required thickness is reached.

Where a better surface finish is required, the first layer of fibre would be fibre tissue rather than the main reinforcing mat which is much coarser in texture. When the fibre and resin are both sprayed, the procedure is as above but the mixture is sprayed in layers onto the gel coat, each layer being rolled or stippled before application of the next layer. The completed moulding is left to cure at room temperature and it may take from several hours to days at 20°C in dry conditions before the product can be demoulded. If the moulding is small enough, heating at 40°–50°C increases the curing rate and the product will have slightly superior properties. The fibre content in contract moulding is usually between 25% and 40%.

The advantages of contact moulding are its relative simplicity, the ability to produce mouldings of large area and the lack of expensive equipment which make the process ideal for short runs, even single mouldings. The disadvantages are its dependence on the skill of the moulder, the low pressure (atmospheric), the inability to mould thickness to close tolerances and the lack of a good surface finish on one side. Working conditions are not pleasant due to the volatility of ingredients and moulding should be carried out in well-ventilated areas.

*Pressure bag moulding* is an improved version of contact moulding in which a pressure is applied to the spray or hand lay-up by means of a pre-shaped inflatable rubber bag (usually neoprene). The pressure gives greater consolidation of the resin/fibre moulding prior to cure, leading to improved properties in the cured product. The second surface is also improved. An alternative to a pressure bag is a *vacuum bag* in which a rubber sheet, pre-shaped if necessary, is laid over the moulding and clamped via a seal to an evacuation system.

Moulds for wet lay-up processes can be made from a variety of inexpensive materials including wood, metal, plaster and plastics. They are commonly made of glass-reinforced polyester by a hand lay-up process using a master pattern of wood or plaster over a wooden frame.

Despite the relatively low degree of reinforcement, contact moulding is still the second most important method of moulding composites in general and glass-reinforced polyesters (GRP) in particular. These are used to manufacture a wide range of products from domestic baths to large boat hulls. GRP (commonly referred to as fibreglass) is now extremely common for rowing boats, pleasure boats, canoes, yachts, dinghies, motor boats, life boats and mine sweepers. The finished boat is light in weight, which makes it attractive to sportsmen and women and it does not corrode or rot like metal and wood. There is increasing use of aramid fibre in boats designed specifically for competitive sport (see section 5.6). GRP mouldings are also widely used in transport where weight saving and easy crash damage repair are the main advantages. Mouldings include complete vehicle bodies (Figure 5.4), lorry cabs as well as components such as farings for motor cycles and cars. The building and construction industries make considerable use of GRP products

**Figure 5.4** Ambulance body moulded in glass-reinforced polyester (fibreglass).

some of which are made by contact moulding. These include roof lights and panels, rain water disposal gutters and ducts.

The use of simple contact moulding techniques is much less widely used with epoxide and phenolic resins. They tend to be used in applications which demand their special merits and thus more sophisticated moulding techniques. Nevertheless, glass/epoxide laminates are used in the manufacture of various tools such as drilling jigs and checking fixtures, moulds for concrete and reaction injection moulding (RIM) of polyurethanes, and as linings for tanks and chimneys.

### 5.5.2 Continuous processes

*Continuous impregnation* is a method of making sheet, usually from polyester and glass. The fibre as CSM is continuously fed with the liquid resin on a moving belt. The fibre/resin mixture is sandwiched between a plastic film and the whole lot is passed through rollers to exclude air and to consolidate the laminate to the required thickness. It is then passed through ovens (80°–90°C) to cure the sheet. The sheet may be convoluted while soft by means of dies or rollers. Rates of production are generally of the order of 1 m/min but rates of 3 m/min are sometimes possible. As an alternative to CSM, cheaper continuous rovings can be used in which case the rovings are cut to suitable lengths and spread onto the bottom film before the resin is applied.

GRP sheet is widely used by the building and construction industries for making panels for roofing, cladding and shuttering and as interior dividing panels.

*Pultrusion* was developed as a process for making products in rod form. Continuous roving is coated with resin by passing the fibre through a resin bath after which the excess resin is removed by, for example, squeeze rolls. If a solvent has been used to obtain an appropriate viscosity in the resin bath, this is also removed. The coated roving is then pulled through a heated forming die and the formed rod is then passed through hot ovens to bring the product to a high degree of cure. Fibre contents of pultrusions are high (up to 85%) and the fibre is uni-axially orientated along the rod length giving the rod high flexural strength and modulus in that direction, especially if carbon fibre is used. Pultrusion is used to make items such as fishing rods, ski-sticks, oars, pole-vaulting poles, radio masts and aerials. Pultrusion is also used for making profiles. These can be subsequently assembled into ladders, walkways and gratings, for example, for use in industrial environments.

A pultrusion development from the USA is the production of pultruded sheet. It is available in thicknesses from 1.5 to 12.7 mm and because it contains a higher fibre content than continuously laminated sheet, pultruded sheet can be made with a 25% weight saving compared with continuously laminated sheet of the same stiffness.

*Filament winding* is essentially a continuous process and is used to manufacture tubular structures of diameter from 4 mm to 6 m. As with pultrusion, resin-coated roving is used. It is wound in layers round a cylindrical or conical mandrel. After curing, the mandrel is removed to leave a hollow moulding. The usual practice is for the mandrel to rotate while a moving feed head traverses the length of the mandrel in each direction until the thickness is achieved. Winding can be circumferential (as on a cotton reel) or helical, the angle of the latter being chosen to give optimum strengths in the hoop direction and along the cylinder length. Glass/polyester windings are the most common and typical applications include industrial and agricultural storage silos, transportation tanks (road and rail), street lamps, telegraph poles and chemical plant (chimneys, pipes, scrubber towers and pressure vessels). In the case of chemical plant, vinyl ester or epoxide resins are often the preferred resins because of the greater resistance to hostile chemical environments. Epoxides are also used where extra strength is required; glass-reinforced filament windings can have hoop strengths of 1.7 GPa. They are used in making components for space and military use such as rocket motor casings, rocket launchers, satellite bodies and deep sea underwater vessels.

Because of the cost of making complete structures by filament winding, a thin filament wound tube is often used as an internal liner in many chemical plant applications. This technique has also been used to renovate ageing sewers.

Cylindrical tubes of up to 6 m diameter can also be made by *centrifugal casting.* Though less strong than equivalent thicknesses of filament wound tube, sufficient strength can be achieved at lower cost for many applications such as general pipework and street lamps.

### 5.5.3 Closed mould processes

Closed moulding techniques are by far the most important processes in use today. They may be classified as resin transfer moulding, compression moulding and injection moulding.

*Resin transfer moulding* (RTM), also known as *resin injection moulding*, is a low cost process involving relatively simple tooling. Fibre mat (CSM, continuous mat or cloth), pre-formed if necessary, is put into one half of a two part mould. The other half is put into position and locked by a mechanical clamping device. The resin, usually polyester, is then injected into the mould from a high shear mixing head, where the initiating system is incorporated, by means of a pumping system. The resin is cold cured under a pressure of 0.1–0.2 MPa. Because of the low pressure, the compaction of the fibre/resin system is little better than with contact moulding but the process has the advantage that two good surfaces are produced and resin handling is avoided. The low moulding pressures and temperatures allow the use of low cost mould materials such as glass-reinforced polyester, aluminium or casting alloys. The mould life depends upon the material but can be useful for making up to 3000 mouldings. Large area mouldings can be produced and with a time saving of between 40% and 80% compared to contact moulding. Mouldings with areas up to 9 m$^2$ have been made but up to 4 m$^2$ is more usual. The process can be used with inserts, with facing panels and to produce sandwich constructions. Typical mouldings include small boats, radomes, freezer cabinets, pools, caravans and large containers.

A related process is *vacuum injection* in which the resin is drawn into the mould by evacuating it. Mould pressures are around 0.1 MPa. The top part of the mould is a flexible membrane (polyethylene has been used) and although the process is cheaper than RTM, part thickness is not so well controlled, one surface is poor and mouldings tend to contain more voids. A pressure-vacuum injection process is also in use which combines the features of RTM and vacuum injection.

One of the principal methods of moulding polyurethanes is similar to RTM and this has been extended to the manufacture of glass mat reinforced rigid foams. The mat (CSM or continuous mat), pre-formed if necessary, is placed in the mould and the polyurethane formulation is dispensed in metered amounts from the mix head into the open mould (*open pour moulding*). The mould is closed and heated at 50°–60°C to bring about foaming and cure. The product is a lightweight reinforced moulding. As an alternative to open pour, the mould may be closed before the resin is injected. Mouldings usually contain 20–30% fibre and surface finish is poor due to the foaming. This can be overcome by covering exposed surfaces either after or during moulding. For example, a pre-formed thermoplastic sheet such as PVC can be inserted against one face of the mould so that the expanding foam adheres to the insert before the resin cures. These glass-reinforced polyurethanes have been developed primarily for the automotive industry where they are used for lightweight vertical panels (interior and exterior), arm rests, trays and covers. Polyurethanes are also moulded round cores to give lightweight mouldings for use in crash padding and bumper components.

*Compression moulding* involves the use of matched die moulds which are placed in a conventional compression press. The fibre and resin are placed in the mould which is then closed under pressure until cure is complete. In its simplest form, the fibre (as mat or cloth) is cut to size and placed in the mould. A measured amount of resin is poured in and the mould is closed. Both cold and hot curing resins are used. Cold curing has the advantage of lower cost since no heating is required. Pressures may be as low as 0.1 MPa, hence cheap mould materials can be used (see RTM). Cycle times are about five times longer than for hot press moulding of the same component and the consolidation of the material is less and often similar to RTM. Cold press moulding is therefore used for short runs (up to 3000) where the highest quality mouldings are not required.

Hot press moulding involves temperatures of 100°–170°C and pressures of 0.35–3.5 MPa. Moulds are usually of high quality tool steel, surface hardened and chrome finished. The quality of the finished product is superior to cold moulding and excellent surface finishes can be obtained. Mechanical properties are also better and dimensional control is excellent. Moulds can be used for over 150 000 mouldings.

The major development in recent years has been the use of DMC and SMC which are based on polyesters or vinyl esters. These compounds are sometimes known as pre-mixes because all of the ingredients are compounded together before dispatch to the moulder. The great advantage of these materials is the ease of handling and speed of moulding to give a consistent product. The compounds are designed for hot moulding (120°–170°C) and when correctly stabilised, they have a shelf-life of about 4 months at 20°C. Both types of compound contain resin, fibre (normally glass) and an inorganic powder filler together with initiators, accelerators, stabilisers and pigments. The SMC has, additionally, a thickening agent.

A DMC will typically contain about 25% resin, 25% fibre and 50% filler such as chalk or china clay. The latter is to provide a dough-like consistency as well as to control shrinkage, thermal expansion and hardness. Table 5.5 shows a typical formulation. Glass fibre lengths are of the order of 50–100 mm and where strength is not so important, the glass fibre can be replaced in part by sisal which imparts a degree of toughness. Grades are available with glass content as high as 40% for high strength and stiffness. The ingredients are compounded in a Z-blade mixer to produce the dough, which

**Table 5.5** Typical moulding compound formulations (figures are parts by weight)

|  | DMC | SMC |
|---|---|---|
| Polyester resin | 30 | 38 |
| Fibre | 18 | 30 |
| Filler | 48 | 55 |
| Pigment | 3 | 3 |
| Release agent | 0.6 | 1.4 |
| Catalyst | 0.3 | 1 |
| Livering agent | — | 2.4 |

is then suitably packaged for dispatch. Alternatively, the dough can be cold extruded to form a rope which is often more convenient to handle. The moulding process involves placing a pre-weighed amount of DMC by hand in the mould and closing the mould under pressures up to 14 MPa. The term *bulk moulding compound* (BMC) is an alternative name for DMC and is more common in Europe and the USA.

SMCs are formulated around chopped strand mat and fibre lengths are usually longer than in DMC because there is no mixing process. Glass content is typically in the range 20–40%. In some cases the fibre is in the form of cloth or continuous roving. The SMC is made by sandwiching the mat between layers of pre-mixed resin paste and passing the sandwich through rollers to impregnate the fibre. The SMC is then rolled with plastic film on both sides into rolls of up to 200 kg. When required for moulding, the appropriate size of sheet is cut off, pre-formed if necessary and moulded under similar conditions to DMC. A typical SMC formulation is shown in Table 5.5.

SMC mouldings have better mechanical properties than DMC due to the longer fibres. Typical properties are shown in Table 5.6. Both can be moulded

**Table 5.6** Properties of compression moulded moulding compounds

|  |  | Polyester | | | | Phenolic | |
|---|---|---|---|---|---|---|---|
|  |  | SMC | | DMC | | SMC* | DMC** |
| Glass content | % | 20 | – 35 | 10 | – 45 | — | — |
| Density | g/cm$^3$ | 1.8 | – 1.9 | 1.8 | – 2.0 | 1.73 | 1.85–2.0 |
| Tensile strength | MPa | 50 | – 95 | 35 | – 55 | 75 | 30 |
| Tensile modulus | GPa | 5 | – 9 | 11 | – 14 | 9 | 9 |
| Flexural strength | MPa | 120 | –170 | 40 | –100 | 160 | 75 |
| Flex modulus | GPa | ~14 | | 10 | – 15 | 8 | 9 |
| Notched Izod | J/12.5 mm | 9 | – 22 | 3 | – 3.5 | 7.6 | 0.64 |
| HDT (1.84 MPa) | °C | 200 | | 200 | | — | — |
| Mould shrinkage | % | 0.005– | 0.2 | 0.005– | 0.2 | 0.05 | — |

* TBA Composites SMC 1030/1130.
** TBA Composites DMC.

with excellent surface finish and mould shrinkage can be as low as 0.005% but is more usually 0.1–0.2%. The low shrink compounds which are also known as *low profile compounds* contain thermoplastic polymers as additives to minimise shrinkage on cure.

DMCs are used in the manufacture of a wide range of electrical equipment such as switch boxes, motor housings, terminal strips, connectors and lamp housings; in domestic and industrial components such as electric iron handles, oven door handles, dishwasher pump housings; and automotive components such as headlamp housings, valve and tappet covers, distributor caps. One of the principal uses of SMC is in the automotive industry where it is used in truck cabs for various panels and trims, bumpers, spoilers, grills step plates and internal components such as storage trays, glove compartments and consoles. The choice of SMC for exterior use is because of its durability, ease of moulding and its ability to withstand painting temperatures of around 150°C. Other uses include components in other forms of commercial transport (road, rail, air and sea), components for the building and construction industries, aerospace and military applications and a variety of housings and trays for industrial and commercial use.

In the USA, there is considerable use of vinyl ester SMC, particularly for automotive components. The mechanical properties are somewhat better than polyester SMC. For example, a 40% glass content SMC can have a tensile strength of around 130 MPa and a flexural strength of just under 300 MPa. Some vinyl ester formulations have a very high glass content (50–65%) and are termed *high strength sheet moulding compounds* (HSMC). Filler content is consequently less and is zero in the case of the 65% glass content sheet. The tensile strengths of these HSMCs are in the range 180–220 MPa with flexural strength in the range 340–430 MPa. This has led to some novel applications such as road wheels for cars.

Some use is being made of phenolic SMCs which, because of their fire retardant properties and low smoke emission when burning, are beginning to replace polyester and vinyl ester SMC in applications where fire is a potential hazard to the public. Phenolic SMCs have a shorter shelf-life than polyester compounds (about 2 months at 20°C) and because of the strong acid curing systems, mould corrosion is a problem. It can be reduced by using acid resistant stainless steel moulds, suitably hardened and hard chrome plated. Any inserts must be acid resistant and brass is recommended. Moulding conditions are similar to polyester SMC with temperatures in the region of 140°–150°C and pressures of 3–6 MPa.

A recent innovation is the production of phenolic DMC by TBA Industrial Products using Norsophen™ resins. These materials are designed at present for compression moulding only and as curing is non-acid, conventional steel moulds can be used. Recommended moulding temperatures are 140°–170°C with pressures of 4–15 MPa. Typical properties of phenolic SMC and DMC are shown in Table 5.6.

*Injection moulding* of suitably formulated polyester DMCs is being increasingly used because of the faster cycle times compared to compression moulding. The DMC is fed to the machine by means of a stuffer unit which replaces the conventional hopper. Barrel temperatures are 20°–25°C and mould temperatures are in the range 130°–170°C. Injection pressures are typically 35 MPa but may be higher.

SMCs are now being injection moulded and the most recent development, announced early in 1989, is the result of a collaboration between Liverpool University and Scott Bader. The formulation involves the use of fibres of up to 25 mm in length and involves conventional SMC production technology. An important difference is the replacement of magnesium oxide by a new additive, marketed as *Impreg*™, as the thickening agent. This produces a sheet with high viscosity and therefore easy handling at room temperatures but which softens on shearing at temperatures over 60°C to give suitably low viscosities for injection moulding. Moulding is performed on standard machines with care being taken to avoid excessive shear. The use of SMC has the advantage of DMC injection moulding with its fast cycle times compared to compression moulding and the advantage of SMC properties in the finished product. Impact strengths, for example, are about twice those obtained with the best injection moulded DMC.

### 5.5.4 Other processes

*Autoclaving* is used for complex mouldings that cannot be easily made by other moulding methods and is suited to the manufacture of small numbers of products. A laminated structure produced by a wet lay-up process is placed in the autoclave, which is a large sealed pressure vessel. Heat and pressure are then applied to allow the laminate to conform to the mould and to effect cure. The pressure is generated by compressed air or nitrogen and is typically about 0.6 MPa. Initial temperatures are in excess of 100°C but cure is effected at lower temperatures over several hours. Autoclaving is used in particular for making high performance composites from carbon- or aramid-reinforced epoxides. An example is the manufacture of bodywork, seats and wings of modern racing cars. The fibre in these applications is usually cloth.

*Pre-preg* is the name given to fibre mattings (either woven or non-woven or roving) that are impregnated with resin prior to use. It allows the use of resins that are too viscous for use in wet lay-up or resin injection and because the pre-preg is dry, handling is facilitated. The impregnation is usually carried out in one of two ways. The most common is to dissolve the resin in a suitable solvent (methyl ethyl ketone (MEK) for epoxides and *iso*-propanol (IPA) for phenolics), impregnate the fibre mat and then remove the solvent in drying ovens. Alternatively, melt impregnation can be used which avoids the possibility of traces of solvent remaining in the pre-preg. When required for use, the dry sheets are cut to shape, pre-formed if necessary, and plied in

**Table 5.7** Processing of reinforced thermoset composites (Western Europe 1986)

| | Tonnes | % |
|---|---|---|
| SMC | 175 000 } | 38 |
| DMC | 70 000 } | |
| Hand lay-up | 168 000 } | 36 |
| Spray lay-up | 65 000 } | |
| Continuous impregnation | 79 000 | 12 |
| Filament winding | 47 000 | 7 |
| Centrifugal methods | 16 000 | 2.5 |
| Others | 25 000 | 4 |

various configurations before curing in a hot press, by autoclaving or by other methods as appropriate. Shelf-lives of pre-pregs can be as short as a month at 20°C depending on the resin used.

The use of pre-pregs allows good control of the fibre content and orientation in the laminate. Uni-directional sheet (from roving) can be plied at various angles, for example, to ensure that appropriate strength and stiffness are achieved in desired directions. Pre-preg tapes are also used to form tubes by a filament winding process.

A major use of epoxide pre-pregs is in printed circuit boards for the electronics industry. They are also used, especially with carbon fibre, for making high strength and stiffness components of low weight for aircraft, space and military use. Where fire and heat resistance are important, a phenolic pre-preg is likely to be preferred. In order to achieve maximum properties, lengthy post-curing sequences at elevated temperatures are common with both epoxide and phenolic pre-pregs.

Polyimide pre-pregs, usually with carbon fibre, are used where very high temperatures are to be encountered. Such pre-pregs when correctly moulded can withstand 275°C continuously. Post-curing is essential and involves temperatures of 200°–350°C over a time period of 12–48 h.

The use of pre-pregs can lead to high strength and modulus composites, even with glass fibre. For example, a ten-layer glass cloth/epoxide laminate can achieve a flexural strength of 420 MPa and modulus of 30 GPa while a 3 mm phenolic/glass cloth can achieve a tensile strength of 550 MPa and modulus of 29 GPa.

Table 5.7 shows the relative importance of the various methods of fabrication.

## 5.6 Sandwich constructions

The design engineer has a great deal of versatility in selecting from fibres, resins and processing methods when designing components from long fibre reinforced systems. This versatility can be extended by using multiple layers in sandwich constructions. One of the major aims in many constructions is to achieve maximum strength/stiffness at minimum weight and this is particularly true of structural components for aircraft and for boats and cars for sport. This can be achieved using the box-girder construction principle, which gives a beam maximum resistance to flexural deflection with minimum weight and is used in the manufacture of aircraft wing components, racing car bodies and yacht hulls, for example. Construction involves laminating thin outer layers of fibre-reinforced resin onto a core material of honeycomb or foamed structure. The composite panel stiffness is due to the fact that when flexed, the skins are in tension or compression while the core is essentially in shear. It is imperative that, for the sandwich to function without failure, the core and skins are properly bonded. Most failures with this type of laminate occur at the interfaces because of the high stress levels there.

Aircraft and racing cars have to withstand forces of several $g$, vibration and torsion, and must be capable of withstanding severe impacts. Such requirements can only be met using multi-component cored structures. The outer skin is usually epoxide with either carbon or aramid or both as cloth (woven or non-woven). The honeycomb in racing cars is usually aluminium but in aircraft components, Nomex-paper honeycomb is also used.

With racing yachts, the tendency has been for narrower hulls to increase performance, with the result that conventionally built boats have required strengthened bulkheads and close-spaced framework to reduce torsional and flexural effects. By increasing the stiffness of the hull sides using sandwich composites, not only is weight saved by using low density materials, but it

**Figure 5.5** Sea King helicopter with rotor blade moulded with sandwich construction (Figure 5.6) (courtesy of Westland Helicopters Ltd, Yeovil).

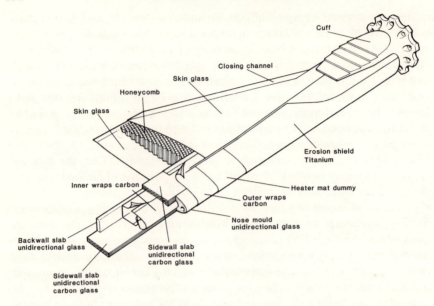

**Figure 5.6** Construction of Sea King helicopter rotor blade (courtesy of Westland Helicopters, Yeovil).

also enables fewer ribs and bulkheads to be used. Depending on the cost of the boat, the core material is balsa wood, PVC or acrylic foam, or aluminium or Nomex honeycomb. The skins themselves are often complex laminates. For example, a glass lay-up of 20% CSM, 20% woven roving and 60% unidirectional roving might be used in one part of the hull while in other parts, where stresses are lower, a simpler construction may be used. Alternatively, a mixture of aramid woven cloth and uni-directional carbon fibres can be used with the carbon fibres aligned at 45° to the cloth. The carbon provides stiffness and the aramid provides impact resistance. Resins are generally polyester or vinyl ester with glass and epoxide with carbon and aramid, but not exclusively.

Helicopter rotor blades of sandwich construction were introduced in the mid-1970s and at the time consisted of glass fibre-reinforced polyester skins round a foamed PVC core. A more recent development is the blade of the Sea King helicopter (Figure 5.5) which is a complex construction based on epoxide pre-preg tape with Nomex™ honeycomb in the trailing edge and polyacrylimide foam on the leading edge. The trailing edge skins are glass-reinforced while the leading edge skin is carbon in an outer layer and glass in the inner layer with side walls of a uni-directional mixture of glass and carbon. Details of construction are shown in Figure 5.6. Of particular note is the method of wrapping the pre-preg tape round the cores. This is done automatically with the tape precision guided by optical devices and the wrapping is stopped when a defined component weight is reached, measured to 0.1% accuracy. The lay-up is then compression moulded at 120°C using aluminium moulds. A later development in the blade design has been the incorporation of a 'swept tip' to the rotor blade which is constructed from modified epoxide glass and carbon fibre pre-pregs consolidated around a polyacrylamide core. These blades have produced a 39% increase in lift when compared with standard blades, as well as giving a marked improvement in fatigue life. The blades, when fitted to a G-Lynx helicopter, have enabled it to achieve the world speed record (249 mph) for helicopters.

## 5.7 Conclusions

The reader will now be aware of the adaptability of the material systems outlined in this chapter. The range of resins, fibres and processing methods provides the designer with a wide choice of combinations for applications ranging from consumer goods to high performance technology. The systems are amenable to large or small number production runs and large size mouldings can be made with relative ease. The future is likely to see an increase in the use of moulding compounds (SMC and DMC), especially in the automotive and other transport industries.

## Further reading

Birley, A. W., Heath, R. J. and Scott, M. J. (1988) *Plastics Materials* (2nd edn.), Blackie, Glasgow.
Brydson, J. A. (1989) *Plastics Materials* (5th edn.), Ilife, London.
*Fibreglass Composites*, Owens Corning Fibreglass (UK) Ltd.
Mascia, L. (1974) *The Role of Additives in Plastics*, Edward Arnold, London.
Wake, W. C. (1977) *Fillers for Plastics*, Iliffe, London.
Seymour, R. B. (1985) In: *Developments in Plastics Technology*, Vol. 2 (ed. Whelan and Craft), Elsevier, London.

# 6  Co-extruded films and containers

J. D. FOX

## 6.1 Introduction

Co-extrusion is the process where two or more polymers are combined while molten, in a single operation, to produce a composite product which retains the separate identity of each starting material in individual layers. The process of co-extrusion is not new and was used in the 19th century for the simultaneous extrusion of graphite and presswood for making pencils. However, it was only in 1964 that co-extruded plastic films were manufactured in America.

### 6.1.1 Processes

Multi-layer films can be manufactured by using a blown or cast film process, multi-layer sheet by using a sheet extrusion process, and multi-layer containers can be manufactured by thermoforming the co-extruded sheet or by an extrusion blow moulding process.

*Blown film.* The co-extrusion blown film line is similar to the monolayer blown film line except that the die is fed by two or more extruders, depending on the number of layers. Hence the die head is very complex requiring a concentric arrangement of the melt channels for each thermoplastic layer. The most important element is the melt distributor whose function is to distribute the incoming melt centrically around the circumference and to let the melt flow emerge at every point at the same rate and temperature.

*Cast film.* As with blown film, the co-extrusion cast film line is similar to the monolayer chill roll film line with the same number of feeding extruders as there are different layers. However, there are two different designs for the co-extrusion die, one a multi-channel die, the other a single channel die in combination with a multi-channel adaptor (the 'feed block system'). The latter is becoming increasingly popular, although a combination of a multi-channel die and feed block is sometimes used.

*Sheet.* The production line for a multi-layer sheet uses either horizontal extrusion or vertical downward extrusion of the melt onto the usual cooling rolls. The choice depends on many parameters, the most important of which is often the thermoplastic material. As with the other processes, the number of sheet layers determines the number of extruders required to feed the die block. The roll stack must be capable of reaching high temperatures for many of the materials in current use. Co-extruded sheet has been used for quite some time and seven layer lines are fairly common. Thermoforming of the sheet produces up to 50% waste and to re-use this material a further one or two layers have to be added to the structure.

*Blow moulding.* As with the other processes the main difference between co-extrusion blow moulding and monolayer blow moulding is the number of extruders used and the design of the cross-head die. There are several different cross-heads available, the most expensive of which has a very sophisticated material distribution system and can handle a wide range of material viscosities. The basic problems of temperature differential, viscosity matching and tie layer compatibility have, as in film and sheet production, been resolved.

### 6.1.2 Materials

Thermoplastic films have gained a dominating position in the field of packaging over several decades, but in the last few years there has been a growing interest in multi-layer co-extruded materials. The co-extrusion process enables properties of different polymers to be combined in one film, and since the requirements of a package cannot always be met by a single layer, there is the possibility of 'tailoring' the packaging material for specific applications. Three and five layer structures are now commonplace while seven and nine layer materials are developing rapidly. The reason for having so many layers is not only for structural and/or barrier properties but also the necessity for adhesive (tie) layers since many thermoplastics do not adhere satisfactorily to each other. Thus, there is a very wide range of multi-layer structures possible; for example, a five layer film could have five components (ABCDE), three components (ABCBA) or four components (AXBXC) where X is a tie layer. Materials which are used in multi-layer structures include: LDPE, LLDPE, HDPE, PP, OPP, PS, HIPS, ABS, SAN, PVC, PC, PU, PA, PVDC, EVOH, PET, acrylics, nitriles. Adhesive tie layers include EVA, SBS, ionomers, PE and PP copolymers.

### 6.1.3 Market area

The co-extrusion of various thermoplastics to produce a variety of multi-layer structures is used to obtain the required overall properties for a specific application. The largest single market is that of the packaging industry, and the European packaging market is now worth about DM100bn, or some 2% of the Gross National Product. The total world market is estimated at some DM500bn. Consumption of packaging materials per head in Europe shows some interesting regional differences (Table 6.1). Predictions for the decade

**Table 6.1** Consumption of packaging materials in Europe (kg/capita).

|          | Tin | Aluminium | Glass | Paper | Corrugated | Card | Plastic |
|----------|-----|-----------|-------|-------|------------|------|---------|
| Germany  | 10  | 1.7       | 47    | 10    | 34         | 8    | 20      |
| France   | 11  | 1.0       | 50    | 10    | 30         | 7    | 15      |
| UK       | 14  | 0.8       | 36    | 8     | 26         | 9    | 14      |
| Italy    | 9   | 1.2       | 32    | 5     | 23         | 7    | 10      |
| Holland  | 23  | 0.5       | 46    | 15    | 27         | 12   | 16      |
| Sweden   | 12  | 0.8       | 12    | 15    | 24         | 12   | 24      |
| Denmark  | 20  | 2.0       | 24    | 25    | —          | 16   | 18      |
| Spain    | 8   | 0.6       | 27    | 5     | 27         | 6    | 9       |
| Portugal | —   | —         | 26    | —     | 15         | 6    | 7       |
| Greece   | —   | —         | 7     | 5     | 16         | 6    | 6       |

**Table 6.2** European drinks market, 1985–1995 (m units).

|            | 1985    | %     | 1995    | %     | % change |
|------------|---------|-------|---------|-------|----------|
| Cans       | 11 431  | 11    | 17 090  | 12    | +4.0     |
| Cartons    | 19 499  | 18    | 29 757  | 21    | +4.5     |
| Glass      | 76 891  | 58    | 69 451  | 49    | −1.0     |
| Plastics   | 10 271  | 12.5  | 24 520  | 17.5  | +9.0     |
| Bag-in-box | 169     | 0.5   | 772     | 0.5   | +16.0    |
| Total      | 118 261 | 100.0 | 141 620 | 100.0 | +1.75    |

1985–1995 show a large increase in plastics consumption with a decrease in glass usage, according to the survey given in Table 6.2.

The major increase in the use of multi-layer co-extruded films for packaging applications in the last few years is in the high barrier film area, particularly for products with high fat content. Bag-in-box systems for oxygen-sensitive liquids such as wine and fruit juices and semi-bulk packaging of tomato paste and fruit purees are also showing high growth. The recent dramatic growth in the sales of microwave ovens in the UK is generating a demand for trays for dual ovens and materials covering the range from minus 8°C to 260°C are now available. While PET is the major material at present, multi-layer structures based on polycarbonate, polyethersulphone and polyetherimide are making in-roads into this area. Co-extruded materials are easily processed through form-fill-seal equipment.

In the blow moulding sector the co-extrusion of containers having the advantages of glass (clarity, retortability and barrier properties) coupled with the advantages of safety (impact resistance), low weight, ease of shaping and printing has led to the opening of new markets in both food and medical areas. Other markets are in the replacement of special papers, and in the co-extrusion of biodegradable polymers, giving packaging which is environmentally friendly.

## 6.2 Reasons for co-extrusion

While co-extrusion has been available for some 25 years, it is only within the last few years that there has been a significant rate of development and market growth of co-extruded multi-layer films, sheet and containers. There are three principle reasons for this. Firstly, the increasing demand for high performance films with improved economics; that is, the higher quality, lower cost trend. Secondly, the developments in polymer chemistry which have generated a wide variety of these high performance polymers and adhesive tie layers. Thirdly, advances in processing equipment which have resulted in improved product quality and consistency. Co-extrusion gives an almost limitless choice for manufacturing products with unique properties.

### 6.2.1 Reasons for co-extrusion

There are almost as many different reasons for co-extrusion as there are products, since the process combines the individual properties of the different polymers used. However, the major reasons can be summarised as follows:

(a) Specific properties can be imparted to a film by co-extruding optimum quantities of polymers (e.g. strength with transparency, high stiffness with high gloss, good weldability with sterilisability, excellent oxygen and gas barrier).
(b) Cost savings in processing since co-extrusion is a one-step process and can eliminate several processing stages (e.g. in coatings and lamination).
(c) Expensive barrier properties can be used in a thin layer (e.g. PVDC, EVOH).
(d) Overall film thickness can be reduced by using a stronger polymer in one or more layers (e.g. in heavy duty bags).
(e) Heterogeneous polymers can be co-extruded with the use of adhesive tie layers (e.g. LDPE and PA).
(f) Special visual and mechanical effects can be produced (e.g. see-through line, one side cling, differential slip).
(g) Use of scrap or reclaim material in the structure to give material cost savings (e.g. refuse sacks).

It is often only by co-extrusion that high performance polymers can be used in an acceptable cost/performance ratio.

### 6.2.2 Advantages of co-extruded films over laminates

Due to the development of improved adhesive tie layers, co-extruded structures now have the equivalent, or often superior, interlayer bond strengths compared to laminates. For example, a metallised polyester laminate bond strength is in the region of 150–500 g/25 mm width, while with a co-extruded film of LLDPE/EVOH, it is usually not possible to separate the layers. An important property for laminates is that of flex crack resistance. High barrier co-extruded films have greater flex crack resistance than laminates which are prone to partial breakdown of the barrier properties due to cracking of the metal layer. Other advantages are: the good clarity of co-extruded films as there is no metal layer in the structure; availability of the film in tubular form; and no solvent retention in the finished film thus eliminating the possibility of tainting the packed product.

### 6.2.3 Advantages of five layer film

One of the significant steps forward in co-extrusion technology was the advent of five layer blown film structures. The advantages these have over three layer films can be summarised as follows:

(a) Improved barrier properties due to the barrier material in the centre being protected against moisture absorption by the outer layers, giving a 40% improvement in barrier properties when the same quantities of material are used.
(b) Raw material cost savings due to a reduction in thickness of the barrier layer and the use of cheaper barrier material, giving approximately 30% saving in total.
(c) Improved processability and conversion due to the use of an outer layer of a polymer with high melting temperature and additives chosen to improve web transport, winding and handling.
(d) Less film curling; with symmetrical film a curl-free flat film is obtained while curling is more easily controlled when using an asymmetrical structure or film with four components.
(e) Easier colouring for food packaging; to prevent colour contaminating food, the inner layer can be clear while the outer layer can be coloured. This is necessary since the barrier and tie layers are unsuitable for colouring because their properties would be affected.
(f) Greater versatility.

### 6.2.4 Disadvantages of co-extrusion

Despite all the reasons for multi-layer structures there are a number of drawbacks and difficulties and these can be summarised as follows:

(a) Product development costs are very high due to the hi-tech state of the art of both materials and equipment and also due to rapidly changing market demands.

(b) Production costs; high costs here include initial choice between blown film and cast film routes, selection of very expensive equipment, costly operation and maintenance of plant and the need for sophisticated quality control and testing.

(c) Short runs are uneconomic; co-extrusion favours a dedicated line and long production runs.

(d) Waste; multi-layer waste is more difficult and expensive to re-use than single layer film (an extra one or two layer structure is required) and the amount can be quite substantial coming from start-up waste, structure change-over waste and set-up waste.

## 6.3 Co-extrusion of blown film

### 6.3.1 Basic process

As stated in the introduction, in blown film co-extrusion two or more extruders feed a single blown film die where separate channels form concentric layers of the different thermoplastics which join just before the die exit. After the die, the multi-layer film passes through a normal film blowing plant and behaves in a similar way to monolayer film. An excellent account of monolayer film production has been given by Whelan and Dunning [1] and thus only those factors of significance to co-extrusion are discussed in this section.

### 6.3.2 Extruder

The universal extruder which can efficiently process all materials has yet to be invented. Extruders are therefore designed so that it is possible to combine various individual components allowing the exchange of screws, feed bushings etc. to be completed in the shortest possible time. To give maximum versatility, the extruders are as small as possible in construction (e.g. with suitably positioned drive motors) and are arranged around the die head taking up minimum space but without making maintenance a nightmare. The barrels are centrifugally cast from extra heavy (41/40) forged steel and are either nitrided or fitted with a proprietary hard carbide alloy liner, the latter giving the barrels a longer life. The screw is driven by a DC motor with an infinitely variable speed; accurate control is especially important at low speeds. The gears used are capable of transmitting a wide range of loads. Grooved or smooth feed bushings are used depending on the material being extruded; grooved bushings for polyolefines, smooth bushings for many high barrier materials.

The output per layer is lower than with single layer lines and the filter systems therefore have smaller screens to prevent low flow speed. The filter surface area is selected for the appropriate extruder size and thermoplastic material, and dynamic flow designs are used for the sensitive materials (barrier and adhesive layers). Cassette type filter systems are usually chosen because of the ease with which they can be changed without displacing the die section. Automatic filter systems do not work satisfactorily due to insufficient streamlining. The distance between the extruder and die head is kept as close as practical, especially for the thermally unstable materials, in order to keep the dwell time of the melt as short as possible.

### 6.3.3 Screw design

Extruder screw design varies considerably for the different thermoplastics used in a multi-layer film and it is vitally important that the correct design is used to obtain optimum processability and product properties. The designs for different materials are well known and documented [2]. However the 'barrier' principle type screw is often used in co-extrusion due to its versatility, excellent mixing characteristics, lower melt temperatures and lower energy consumption compared with alternative screws. This type of screw has approximately one-third feed, one-third transition with barrier, and one-third meter/mix. The centre section has a channel of decreasing volume which is adjacent to a melt channel of increasing volume resulting in the separation of melt from solids. As can be seen from Figure 6.1 in a conventional screw (left) the melt contains unmelted granules. In the barrier screw (right) the melt is forced over the barrier flight into the conveying channel, and thus has an added shear component. The solids left in the diminishing plasticising channel are melted with a uniform plasticisation while the steady increase in the conveying channel volume maintains a neutral pressure profile.

### 6.3.4 Die design

The heart of the co-extrusion system is the die which, by its nature, is

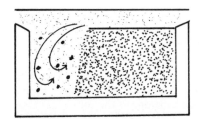 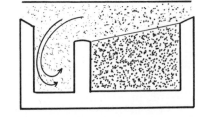

**Figure 6.1** Solids melting in different types of screw.

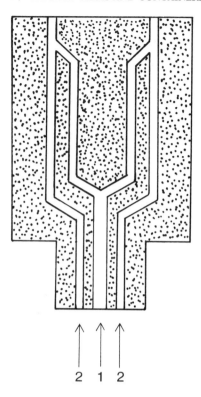

2   1   2

**Figure 6.2** Two layer film die.

necessarily far more complex than that of a single layer die. The material from each extruder enters its own spiral chamber at the bottom of the die and the individual layers are then combined within the final section prior to emerging as a common tube. Typical constructions for two, three and four layer film die heads are shown in Figures 6.2, 6.3 and 6.4. The die has to deal with a very wide range of thermoplastics each with its specific rheological, thermal and chemical properties. The more divergent these properties are, the greater the difficulties.

Materials that exhibit wide differences in viscosity are particularly difficult to handle. They can diminish optical properties and introduce machine direction gauge variations. It is crucial to match the velocities of the different materials as closely as possible where the layers converge in order to avoid interfacial flow instability and to give optimum properties. The thickness uniformity of the thin layers of barrier and tie materials must be very carefully controlled as these are often only 5 μm thick. There must also be a balance between having sufficient contact time under pressure to promote interlayer

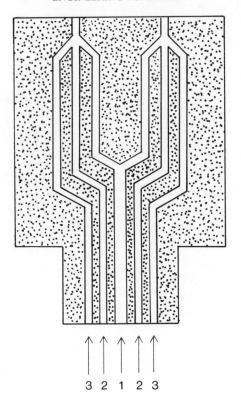

3 2 1 2 3

**Figure 6.3** Three layer film die.

adhesion and having excessive residence times which result in the migration of the lowest viscosity materials into specific bands around the circumference of the die. Die temperature control is a very important aspect because of the different polymer viscosities and degradation temperatures. Dies are available with individual temperature control for specific sections while others have thermal insulation between each polymer layer giving the optimum processing conditions for each material. It is also important that the dies are designed for maximum streamlining as many of the barrier and adhesive materials are particularly prone to degradation.

There are a number of die designs to accommodate these features but all are based on the spiral mandrel distribution system used in monolayer film dies. Details are outside the scope of this review of co-extrusion but spirals with overlapping eight port entries and flow mixing channels are currently being developed. Many die heads are designed to give easy changes of dies with different diameters to enable the film width to be altered in a ratio of approximately 1:1.3 to 1:2.5 as the blow ratio for the multi-layer films is

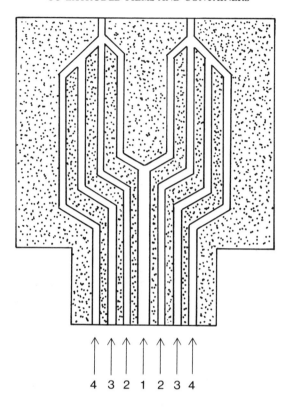

4 3 2 1 2 3 4

**Figure 6.4** Four layer film die.

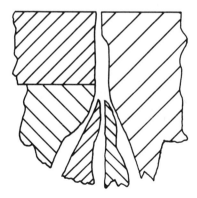

**Figure 6.5** (courtesy of Betol Machinery).

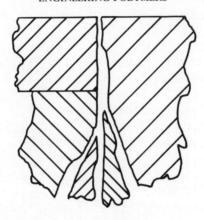

**Figure 6.6** (courtesy of Betol Machinery).

limited to 1.2:1 to 4:1. Figures 6.5, 6.6 and 6.7 show how the melt streams are combined in three different ways. Figure 6.5 shows the layout for compatible materials with a single top ring adjustment; Figure 6.6 shows the layout for two incompatible materials with a central adhesive layer; Figure 6.7 shows the layout for either compatible or incompatible materials where three adjusting rings give complete control over each layer thickness. Design and evaluation of hundreds of dies has allowed computer simulation programs to

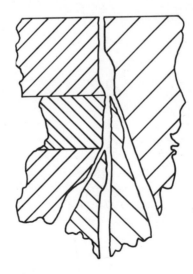

**Figure 6.7** (courtesy of Betol Machinery).

be developed and while this has made a substantial impact, experience and 'art' still play a large role in the design of co-extrusion dies.

As with monolayer plant, a rotating or oscillating die is used to obtain even surface geometry of the film. For multi-layer film, a special rotator has been developed which is a complete unit in itself and is independent of the die, die size and number of layers. This rotator accepts different types of dies and has an infinitely variable rotational speed governed by a DC motor. This device is very reliable and the sealing rings only need replacing during a twice yearly general cleaning operation. For small extruder sizes some machinery manufacturers supply a rotary platform to rotate the entire extrusion unit.

### 6.3.5 Film cooling, collapsing and winding

The components following the die are similar to those of a normal blown film line. Cooling is effected by means of the dual-lip system using high volume, low pressure air, combined with internal bubble cooling (IBC) to give maximum output.

Due to the variety of thermoplastics used, each with its particular film stiffness, surface frictional behaviour and temperature, the bubble collapsing system has to be modified to prevent sticking and wrinkling of the film. A combination of collapsing boards and rolls is sometimes used. Similarly, different winders are required depending on the materials being processed and a combination of contact and centre winding principles is used. During centre winding, the centre winding shaft is driven while the contact winding shaft runs with a low torque. In combination operation, it is the contact drive which drives with a high torque. Switch-over to centre winding is recommended when winding thick or sticky films or films sensitive to tension.

### 6.3.6 Process control

The usual total film thickness and width control systems are used with co-extrusion film lines and there are a number of very sophisticated fully automatic systems available. However, no continuous measurement of the individual layers is yet available although some off-line gauges are used and development of these for on-line versions is currently being undertaken by a number of firms. One system uses infrared sensing. This basically involves measuring the infrared absorption by the different layers but it has a fundamental drawback in that similar materials (or dissimilar materials with similar absorption characteristics) cannot easily be distinguished. Another method relies on the phenomenon of light being reflected as it passes through a layer of one refractive index into a layer of a different refractive index. A gauge collects these reflections and superimposes them so that they form an interference pattern with the distances between the interference bands related to the distances between the material interfaces. This method also has some restrictions as it needs a definite interface between materials, a difference in refractive index of at least 10% and transparency to light.

Due to the lack of continuous measurement of individual layers a system is used, quite effectively, which measures the output of each extruder. Production data such as line speed, film width and throughput are fed to a microprocessor which computes the actual weight of each layer from that information. It is also fed the required values and if there is a difference between these two values then it adjusts the screw speed, etc., of the individual extruders.

## 6.4 Co-extrusion of cast film

### 6.4.1 Basic process

The cast film process, whether monolayer or multi-layer, involves extruding polymer melt through a flat die downwards on to chilled rolls which cool the material to below its melting point. The film is then handled through the plant passing, as appropriately installed, through gauges (infrared or beta), treaters (single- or double-sided) and on to a winding and slitting system selected for the relevant end-use. While the process is fundamentally different from the blown film process (a detailed comparison is given later), the extruder and screw design details given in section 6.3 are the same for both processes. Co-extrusion technology for cast films is now very well established with many production lines running five, seven or nine layer barrier structures.

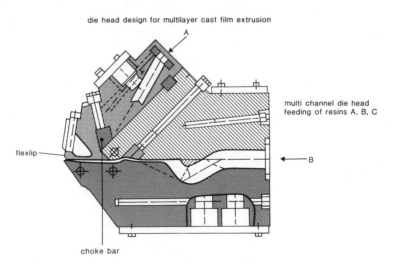

**Figure 6.8** Die head design for multi-layer cast film extrusion (redrawn from figure courtesy of Reifenhäuser GMBH).

### 6.4.2 *Die design*

There are two types of die for the co-extrusion of cast film. These are the multi-channel die, shown in Figure 6.8, and the 'feed block system' which uses a single channel die in combination with a multi-channel adaptor block (Figure 6.9). The feed block system is widely used for the co-extrusion of

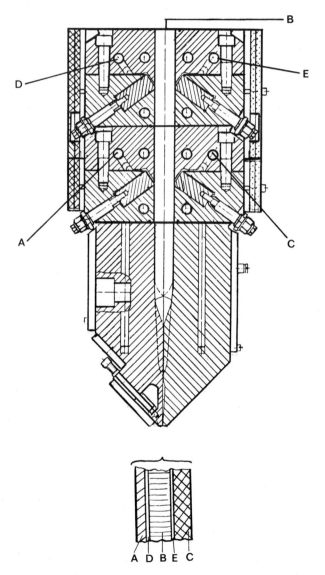

**Figure 6.9** Single channel die head with multi-channel adapter, 'feedblock' feeding of resins A, B, C, D, E (courtesy of Reifenhäuser GMBH).

similar thermoplastics. There are two reasons for this. Firstly, investment costs are lower than for the multi-channel die and, secondly, the thickness of the layers can be readily altered by adjusting or exchanging the choker bars. It is important to ensure that laminar flow occurs between materials and that no mixing takes place within the die. Designs are now available that can handle materials with viscosities as different as 40:1. Using such a feed block it is possible to achieve maximum adhesion of the tie layers by having a long contact time at the correct temperature. The multi-channel die is used when extruding thermoplastics of different types, or additionally, materials with large differences in viscosity.

### 6.4.3 Film cooling, handling and winding

Rapid and uniform cooling of the melt is important to minimise crystallisation to give optimum optical properties. This requires a critical relationship between chill roll temperature, roll size, speed of rotation and degree of contact between melt and rolls. As with the monolayer line, good contact between the melt and chill rolls is achieved by an air knife, and edge-pinners (pressurised air or electrostatic charging systems) minimise the draw-down effect.

The rest of the co-extruded cast film line is essentially the same as the monolayer line with DC drives, automatic web tension, flying knife system for reel core changing and sophisticated winders. The direct re-cycling of scrap from edge-trimming is possible when extruding similar thermoplastics and the waste is fed back to the primary extruder via a granulating system. Gear pumps are sometimes fitted between the extruder and the feed block to increase melt flow stability when re-cycling scrap as this can vary in density.

### 6.4.4 Process control

Computerised systems are available for co-extruded cast film lines, within the limitations discussed in section 6.3.6. Automatic control of the total film thickness is by use of thermal expansion bolts operating the flexible lips; these are triggered by a signal from the automatic thickness gauge control system.

### 6.4.5 Comparison with blown film

Both the blown film and cast film processes are well known but there are significant differences especially when considering co-extrusion. These may be summarised thus:

(a) *Space requirement*: cast film lines require much greater floor space than blown film lines but the latter need greater roof height. If outputs are compared then floor areas are similar.

(b) *Output*: cast film lines have substantially greater outputs than blown film lines due to the inherent slow cooling of the latter system. Cast film lines can reach production rates of up to 300 m/min, while blown film lines are usually less than half this figure.

(c) *Film width*: because of the very different types of die used, the width of film produced from blown lines is much greater than that from cast film lines. Widths of up to 18 m are available from blown film extrusion while 3 m widths are the maximum obtained from cast film extrusion; there is no edge-trimming with the blown film process.

(d) *Gauge control*: the tolerances for total film thickness are dependent on the thermoplastics used and also on the film width but generally for blown film are:

$$0.010\text{–}0.040 \text{ mm} \quad \pm 12\%$$
$$0.040\text{–}0.100 \text{ mm} \quad \pm 10\%$$
$$0.100\text{–}0.250 \text{ mm} \quad \pm 8\%$$

For cast film, the tolerances are some 50% better than these due to the difference between the blown and cast film dies and also due to problems with bubble stability.

(e) *Shape of film*: for bag making, tubular film is required and this can only be made by the blown film process.

(f) *Production flexibility*: it is easier to change the width of blown film than that of cast film and hence the former gives greater production flexibility. It is also more suited to short runs than the cast film line.

(g) *Film properties*: cast film has superior clarity, lower rigidity and is glossier and softer than blown film. Blown film is bi-axially orientated and cast film uni-axially orientated which has a number of effects on the physical properties of the films. While impact strength is increased for blown film, other property values depend on whether they are measured in the machine direction (MD) or the transverse direction (TD). Elongation at break, tear strength and heat stability are all increased in the MD for blown film but increased in the TD for cast film. Tensile strength is increased in the MD for cast film but decreased for blown film, while it is decreased in the TD for cast film and increased for blown film.

(h) *Economics*: it is not sensible to make direct economic comparisons between these two processes unless a specific application is considered. However, large blown film units are relatively cheaper to buy than cast film units, while operational costs are lower for the latter systems and when looking at economics of scale, cast film lines are probably cheaper above about 4000 tonnes per annum output.

## 6.5 Co-extrusion of sheet

The main difference between co-extrusion of sheet and co-extrusion of cast film is the thickness of the film. In general the thickness range for sheet is between 300 µm and 12 mm, and the width range between 600 mm and 3000 mm. The thickness tolerances are between 2% and 3%, and the production rate between 15 m/min and 30 m/min.

While both the horizontal extrusion and vertical downward extrusion techniques are possible, most co-extrusion sheet lines use the horizontal feeding system as many of the thermoplastics require short dwell times and hence short melt flow channels. For similar reasons, the feed block system is usually used. Otherwise the details are exactly as for cast film but, due to the slower production rates, the handling and winding systems are not quite so critical.

Sheet gauge measurement equipment is operated on either a monitoring basis or as a control system where the gauge is coupled via an on-line computer to an automatic die.

Most multi-layer sheet is thermoformed out-of-line from the extruder unlike many in-line monolayer sheet systems. The principal reason for this is that out-of-line production gives greater flexibility for both the extrusion and thermoforming processes. It allows constant monitoring and quality control of the extruded sheet together with easier maintenance. Out-of-line thermoforming is also more sensible for shorter production runs.

## 6.6 Co-extrusion blow moulding

The techniques developed for co-extrusion of thermoplastic films have been adopted for the blow moulding of hollow articles. As with those processes, the extruders are arranged radially to feed a common extrusion head where the materials are brought together in a steady phase without intermixing. The technology has developed rapidly and three to six layer structures are common. Figure 6.10 shows a typical structure of a six layer container. The basic plant and operation is the same as for normal extrusion blow moulding apart from the die head, and since the former has been adequately covered in the literature [3], only the die head design is discussed here.

A number of very differently designed heads have been used successfully. For example, the Ando head is small, simple to strip, can be run at various temperatures along its length and is less expensive then the Bekum unit. However, the Bekum head has a more sophisticated material distribution system and can handle materials having a wide range of viscosities. The Krupp Kautex method to produce a parison by means of a heart-curved torpedo puts the weld at the most favourable part of the parison ensuring a good wall thickness distribution.

The manufacture of co-extrusion heads is carried out on computerised numerical control (CNC) machinery and thus extremely low, constant tolerances are achieved. From the design point of view, it is unimportant in which order the layers are built up within the die head. However, the order

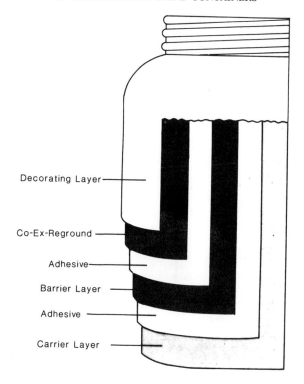

Decorating Layer

Co-Ex-Reground

Adhesive

Barrier Layer

Adhesive

Carrier Layer

**Figure 6.10** Structure of six layer packaging (redrawn from figure courtesy of Krupp Kautex)

does effect the pinch-off area. With a multi-layer structure where the internal layer is the barrier layer, a weakness can occur in the pinch seam at the base of the moulding. The pinch-off area depends for strength on the thickness of the innermost layer. If this is a very thin barrier layer, faults can occur. This is shown in Figure 6.11.

There is considerable production waste and the re-usability of this process scrap is of the greatest importance for the economic success of co-extrusion. The mixing of the re-granulated material with bonding agents decreases the adhesive strength considerably and is therefore not done. It is possible to incorporate the scrap in the carrier layer, but more often it is included as a separate layer with maybe the addition of a further adhesive layer (see Figure 6.10).

Machine control is another very significant economic factor for co-extrusion blow moulding. Parison control devices are all important and are regulated by the conventional contactor system or a microcomputer system.

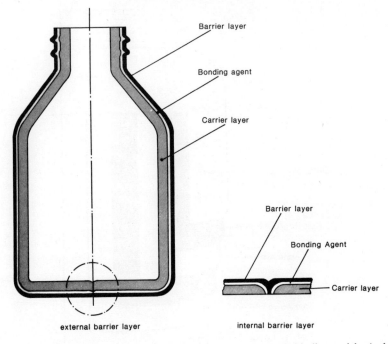

**Figure 6.11** Construction of the pinch seam in three layer co-extruded hollow articles (redrawn from figure courtesy of Krupp Kautex).

For the parison length control, a specially developed cascade system permits the synchronised adjustment of all extruder speeds in correct relation to each other. Needless to say, co-extrusion blow moulding is a very expensive process with the major proportion of costs coming from the die head unit and from the special raw materials. The accurate control of layer thickness and re-use of process scrap is vital to the operation.

## 6.7 Materials, properties and applications

### 6.7.1 Material combinations and interlayer adhesion

As stated earlier, co-extrusion gives the possibility of tailoring a film, sheet or container for a specific application. While it is theoretically feasible to combine any thermoplastic material in a structure, many polymers do not adhere to each other and thus there is a need for adhesive tie layers. Of the 20 or so polymers currently used in co-extrusion (see section 6.1.2) only a few of these adhere sufficiently to each other to be co-extruded without the use of a tie layer. These are materials which have a similar base chemical structure. A guide to material bonding is given in Table 6.3.

The development of adhesive tie layers has played a vital role in the

| Material | Olefins | | | Styrenes | | | | | | PVCs | | Misc. | | | | | Adhesives | | |
|---|---|---|---|---|---|---|---|---|---|---|---|---|---|---|---|---|---|---|---|
| | LDPE | HDPE | PP | Low-impact PS | Medium-impact PS | High-impact PS | Crystal PS | ABS** | ABS | Rigid PVC | Flexible PVC | Polycarbonate | Polyurethane | Acrylic | Nitriles | Nylon 6 | EVA | Ionomers | SBS |
| **Olefins** | | | | | | | | | | | | | | | | | | | |
| LDPE | G | G | G | P | P | P | P | P | P | P | P | P | P | P | P | P | G | G | G |
| HDPE | G | G | G | P | P | P | P | P | P | P | P | P | P | P | P | P | G | G | G |
| PP | G | G | G | P | P | P | P | P | P | P | P | P | P | P | P | P | G | P | G |
| **Styrenes** | | | | | | | | | | | | | | | | | | | |
| Low-impact PS | P | P | P | G | G | G | G | G | P | P | P | F | P | P | P | P | G | ? | G |
| Medium-impact PS | P | P | P | G | G | G | G | G | P | P | P | F | F | F | P | P | G | ? | G |
| High-impact PS | P | P | P | G | G | G | G | G | P | P | P | F | F | G | P | P | G | ? | G |
| Crystals PS | P | P | P | G | G | G | G | G | P | P | P | F | F | G | P | P | G | ? | G |
| ABS** | P | P | P | G | G | G | G | ? | ? | G | G | F | G | G | G | G | G | ? | G |
| ABS | P | P | P | P | P | P | P | ? | ? | G | G | F | G | G | P | G | G | ? | P |
| **PVCs** | | | | | | | | | | | | | | | | | | | |
| Rigid PVC | P | P | P | P | P | P | P | G | G | G | G | U | U | G | U | U | G | ? | G |
| Flexible PVC | P | P | P | P | P | P | P | G | G | G | G | U | U | G | U | U | G | ? | ? |
| **Misc.** | | | | | | | | | | | | | | | | | | | |
| Polycarbonate | P | P | P | F | F | F | F | F | F | U | U | G | G | G | ? | ? | ? | ? | F |
| Polyurethane | P | P | P | P | F | F | F | G | G | U | U | G | G | G | ? | ? | ? | ? | F |
| Acrylic | P | P | P | P | F | G | G | G | G | G | G | G | G | P | P | ? | F | ? | F |
| Nitriles | P | P | P | P | P | P | P | G | P | U | U | ? | ? | P | G | G | P | G | P |
| Nylon 6 | P | P | P | P | P | P | P | G | G | U | U | ? | ? | ? | G | G | G | P | G |
| **Adhesives** | | | | | | | | | | | | | | | | | | | |
| EVA | G | G | G | G | G | G | G | G | G | G | G | ? | ? | F | P | G | G | ? | ? |
| Ionomers | G | G | P | ? | ? | ? | ? | ? | ? | ? | ? | ? | ? | ? | G | P | ? | G | ? |
| SBS | G | G | G | G | G | G | G | G | P | G | ? | F | F | F | P | G | ? | ? | G |

\* G = good; F = fair; P = poor; ? = unknown; U = undesirable.
\*\* Less than 20% acrylonitrile content.

commercialisation of co-extrusion. A good bond strength is not only required at normal temperatures but also at elevated temperatures; for instance, where materials are used on form-fill-seal equipment or during sterilisation of the product. The tie layer must be processable at the required temperature and compatible with the viscosities of the other materials in the structure. In addition, the tie layer must be clear and non-yellowing. To achieve all these requirements, a great deal of research and development has been carried out and is still continuing. A number of companies now produce tie layers but are understandably reluctant to release details of their products. Most of the tie layers are based on EVA, SBS, ionomers, and PE and PP copolymers. As an example, one chemically modified PP copolymer formulation has been specifically designed for bonding PP to EVOH and PA. It can also be used for metals and cellulosic substrates. It can be used on all types of co-extrusion equipment (film, sheet and blow moulding) and gives best results when processed at temperatures below 230°C. It has low odour and taste transfer, very low water absorption and meets FDA requirements. Acid anhydride modified PE is used to give a high interlayer bond strength between PE and EVOH. For reasons of cost and overall product thickness, these tie layers are kept as thin as possible, often in the region of 5 μm.

### 6.7.2 Properties and applications

Co-extruded film and sheet and co-extruded blow moulded products are most widely used in the packaging industry where there is a large diversity of requirements. There are often demands for high barrier characteristics against, for example, oxygen, carbon dioxide or water vapour in areas such as the cosmetic, pharmaceutical and chemical industries. There may equally be demands for good mechanical properties such as tensile strength, impact resistance or stiffness while other applications may require excellent optical properties such as clarity, high gloss or low haze. Other properties that might be specified could be resistance to oil and solvents, antistatic properties, weather resistance and light stability. Similarly, requirements such as heat stability, ease of printing or sterilisability may be needed. The possibilities and combinations are almost infinite! No one thermoplastic has a variable combination of such properties, hence the unique position of co-extruded materials.

### 6.7.3 High barrier products

High barrier refers to a low permeability to gases, especially oxygen. As can be seen from Table 6.4, the commonly used thermoplastics for packaging show high permeability values for oxygen whereas EVOH, PVDC and PET provide the best oxygen barriers. EVOH under dry conditions (it is sensitive to humidity due to the hygroscopic nature of the vinyl alcohol content of the

**Table 6.4** Oxygen transmission rate ($cm^3$ $O_2/m^2$ of film 20 μm thick for 24 h under atmospheric pressure at 23°C and 0% relative humidity)

|  | $cm^3$ $O_2/m^2$ |
|---|---|
| Aluminium foil | 0 |
| EVOH (32% ethylene) | 0.2 |
| EVOH (38% ethylene) | 0.6 |
| EVOH (44% ethylene) | 1.8 |
| PVDC | 3.2 |
| PVDC coated PP | 13 |
| PAN | 16 |
| Orientated PA6 | 33 |
| Orientated PET | 46 |
| Amorphous PA6 | 50 |
| PA6 | 100 |
| UPVC | 260 |
| HDPE | 3000 |

copolymer) is the best oxygen barrier of any co-extrudable polymer. It also has excellent oil and solvent resistance, has high gloss and low haze, is light stable and weather resistant. It is therefore widely used in five layer structures with LLDPE (requiring a tie layer because of its poor adhesion with LLDPE) to provide an excellent combination of properties. A typical structure is ABCBA, where

A is LLDPE    at 35 μm
B is tie layer    at  5 μm
C is EVOH    at 10 μm
B is tie layer    at  5 μm
A is LLDPE    at 35 μm

The structure could equally be ABCBD, where D is another polyolefine at the same thickness giving a range of possible properties.

EVOH has limited mechanical properties and the outer layers have to compensate for its lack of strength. The EVOH layer must not be too thick as this can cause flex crack problems. Other materials used with EVOH are PA, PC, PET and PS. Barrier packaging using EVOH includes applications such as retort, hot-fill and aseptic packaging in film, pouches, bottles and thermo-formed sheet. Bag-in-box systems are a fast growing packaging method finding applications in retail and industrial markets. These extend from small 3–20 l size packs for wine and fruit juices to 200–1000 l size packs for tomato paste and fruit purees. Other foods include sauces, salad dressings, apple products, meat, cheese and fish products. Further applications are packaging of pesticides, and for medical, pharmaceutical and chemical products. For some of these applications, the EVOH films are laminated to a range of

**Table 6.5** Résumé of materials, properties and applications for two, three and five layer structures.

| Material combination | Special properties | Applications |
| --- | --- | --- |
| **Two layer structures** | | |
| LDPE/LDPE | High puncture resistance, two colours | Milk pouches, carrier bags, medical packaging |
| LDPE/LDPE recycle | High resistance at low thickness | Carrier bags |
| LDPE/HDPE | High strength | Waste bags, packaging for pastries, rock salt, peat, fertilisers |
| LDPE/LDPE foam | Different colours, low weight | Boutique bags |
| LDPE/LLDPE<br>LLDPE/LLDPE | Excellent transparency, good adhesion | Stretch wrap film for pallet packaging |
| LLDPE/PP | Good strength at low thickness | Carrier bags |
| LLDPE/HDPE | Weldable, sterilisable, good strength | Blister packs, sterilisable packs, protective films for glass |
| LDPE/EVA | Tough at low temperature, transparent | Packaging for dairy products, frozen foods, medical goods |
| LDPE/ionomer | Weldable, sterilisable, high strength | Linings for carton boxes, blood plasma bags, bakery packaging |
| HDPE/EVA | | Sliced cheese packs |
| PP/EVA | Weldable, oil resistant | Packaging for bakery goods and coconuts |
| EVA/ionomer | | Salted meat packs |
| PA/PA | Tough at low temperature, good barrier | Packaging for deep frozen foods, meat, fish, sausages, ham, cheese |
| PA/ionomer | Thermoformable, good printability | Disposable cups, picnic ware, packaging for dairy products and ice |
| PS/SB | | Bag-in-box, medical envelopes |
| PC/ionomer | | |
| **Three layer structures** | | |
| LDPE/LDPE/LDPE | Different colours, nacre effect | Boutique bags |
| LDPE/LDPErecycle/LDPE | Weldable | Carrier bags, waste bags |
| LDPE/LDPE/PP | | Stretch wrap film for pallet packaging |
| LDPE/HDPE/LDPE | High resistance at low thickness | Carrier bags |
| LDPE/HDPErecycle/LDPE | Weldable, high strength, stiff | Heavy duty bags, waste bags, packaging for cereals and pastries |
| LDPE/PP/LDPE | | Packaging for chips and bread |
| LDPE/HDPErecycle/HDPE | Weldable, high strength, stiff | Heavy duty bags, waste bags |
| LDPE/HDPE/LLDPE | Weldable, high strength | Carrier bags, milk powder packs |
| LDPE/HDPErecycle/LLDPE | High strength at low thickness | Carrier bags |
| LDPE/LLDPE/LLDPE | High strength, transparent | Industrial stretch film |
| LLDPE/LLDPE/LLDPE | High puncture resistance, good adhesion | Heavy duty bags |
| LLDPE/LDPErecycle/LLDPE | Weldable, good strength | Refuse sacks |

| Structure | Properties | Application |
|---|---|---|
| LLDPE/HDPE/LLDPE | High resistance at low thickness | Carrier bags |
| LLDPE/PP/LLDPE | High resistance at low thickness | Carrier bags, industrial bags |
| HDPE/LDPE/HDPE | | Packaging for baked confectionery products |
| LDPE/foamed LDPE/LDPE | Low weight, soft feel, insulant | Exclusive carrier bags, delicate packaging |
| LDPE/LDPE/EVA | Good barrier, UV resistant, multicoloured | Packaging for sweets, plants, bakery products |
| LDPE/HDPE/EVA | Slip and anti-slip properties in/out layers | Industrial bags |
| LDPE/EVA/PP | No sticking during shrink wrapping | Shrink wrapping, packaging for pastries and bakery goods |
| LDPE/EVA/K RESIN | | Thermoadhesive protective films for glass |
| LDPE/tie/PA | Good barrier properties | Packaging for meat, ham, cheese, fish, milk, pre-cooked meals |
| LDPE/ionomer/PA | | Packaging for smoked fish and delicatessen goods |
| LDPE/ionomer/PC | Transparent, sterilisable, opaque to UV light | Packaging for medical products |
| PP/ionomer/PC }<br>PP/LDPE/EVA | | Packaging for baked confectionery goods |
| PP/tie/PVDC }<br>PP/tie/EVOH | Thermoformable, good barrier properties | Containers for pasteurisation and sterilisation of foodstuffs |
| Ionomer/tie/PA | Low temperature and high seal strengths | Seal packs, packaging for oil and fatty products |
| EVA/PP/EVA | Weldable, sterilisable | Packaging for dehydrated vegetables |
| PS/SB white/PSrecycle | Rigid, high surface gloss | Containers for milk and milk products |
| PS/recycle/HIPS | | |
| PA/ionomer/PC | Transparent, sterilisable, UV resistant | Bag-in-box packaging, medical envelopes |

**Five layer structures**

| Structure | Properties | Application |
|---|---|---|
| LDPE/tie/PA/tie/LDPE<br>LDPE/tie/PA/tie/PP<br>LDPE/tie/PA/tie/ionomers<br>LDPE/tie/PA/tie/EVA } | Good barrier properties, weldable, transparent | Packaging of meat, cheese, sausages, ham, ready-cooked meals shrink wrapping |
| LDPE/tie/EVOH/tie/LDPE<br>LDPE/tie/EVOH/tie/PP | Good barrier properties, transparent | Packaging of foodstuffs requiring high barrier properties |
| LDPE/tie/EVOH/tie/ionomers<br>LDPE/tie/EVOH/tie/EVA } | Excellent oxygen and gas barrier | Bag-in-box wine packs, bags for fish meals |
| PP/tie/PVDC/tie/PP | Good barrier giving long shelf-life | Containers for food packaging |
| EVA/tie/PA/tie/PAcopol<br>EVA/tie/EVOH/tie/PAcopol } | Excellent barrier properties | Packaging of meat, pre-cooked meals, milk powder<br>Packaging of medical items |
| PC/tie/EVOH/tie/PP | High strength, excellent barrier | Blow moulded containers for food and medical items |

N.B.  In many cases LDPE is often replaced by LLDPE with slightly different properties.

substrates which include paper, polyester, cellophane and nylon, providing both a high barrier and a heat-seal layer in the one film.

### 6.7.4 Food packaging products

For normal food packaging, structures with polyolefines and nylons are commonly used. A typical combination is ABCBD, where

| | | |
|---|---|---|
| A is LLDPE | at | 25–35 μm |
| B is tie layer | at | 5 μm |
| C is PA6 | at | 20 μm |
| B is tie layer | at | 6 μm |
| D is EVA | at | 30–40 μm |

These multi-layer films are used for cheese, sausages, fish, bacon, ham, milk powder, peanuts etc. Foods with a high fat or oil content require a special inner layer which can be sealed even if it is contaminated by oil. For such applications the inner layer is usually an ionomer and a typical structure is ABCBD, where A is the ionomer, B the tie layer, C is PA6 and D is LLDPE, with a total thickness of 100 μm.

### 6.7.5 Stretch film

Stretch film is made by cast co-extrusion and is usually a three layer structure of LDPE/LLDPE/LDPE. The middle layer thickness is about 13 μm with the outer layers about 5 μm thick. The film is transparent and has good strength at high extensibility and is widely used as stretch wrap film for pallet packaging. Normally the film has a no cling outer surface which allows close stacking of pallets. Thin films are used, for example, for stacking empty PET bottles while thicker films give good stability for heavy items on the pallets. Some stretch film is now being cast co-extruded by direct injection of polybutylene fluid into the extruder barrel. Up to 8% of polybutylene is added in this way and the injection process, replacing the blending of pre-compounded tack rich material in the hopper, has reduced costs and increased homogenisation. Co-extruded cast polyolefine film is also used in form-fill-seal applications (cereals, biscuits, powder products as well as non-food applications) and for laminating with paper, foil, polyester, cellulose or other thermoplastics.

### 6.7.6 Co-extruded containers

Co-extruded sheet used for thermoforming is normally either a three or five layer structure, but can have as many as nine layers. For example, sheet for the thermoforming of milk containers is made from PS/ABS/re-cycled material with thicknesses of 30/600/370 µm, respectively, giving a very stiff material with a high gloss surface. Colour differentials can also be introduced, for example a three layer structure of white PS/scrap/brown high gloss HIPS for disposable table wear, giving cups with different colours inside and out. Containers for food packaging are often five layer combinations, for example PP/tie/PVDC/tie/PP with thicknesses of 700/20/160/20/700 µm, respectively. This structure has excellent gas barrier properties with a shelf-life of more than 12 months. Other materials used for similar applications are PC, PET and EVOH. A three layer structure that is beginning to compete with CPET for dual oven trays is polyetherimide/PC/polyetherimide. Blow moulded containers include PC/EVOH/PP structures which meet the severe requirements of the food and medical industries.

This account of different material combinations represents only a fraction of the possible film structures but it does show that the co-extrusion process permits selection of thermoplastic materials to satisfy the required applications. Table 6.5 summarises the characteristics of two, three and five layer structures.

## 6.8 Conclusions

Over the last 25 years co-extrusion has become an integral part of the plastics processing industry. From the production of a rather crude two layer film structure, it has developed rapidly to the point where seven and nine layer lines are fairly common and six layer containers widely used. The demand for high performance films and containers with improved economics will ensure that this growth will continue to be met by new polymers, new adhesive tie layers and further advances in processing equipment. The basic problems associated with co-extrusion, that of polymer viscosity matching, temperature differentials and tie layer compatibility, have largely been resolved. The control technology of layer thickness is developing continuously and this will lead to further reductions in both material thickness and costs. The re-use of process scrap is an area where more research is required as this waste material accounts for a high proportion of production costs.

## References

1 Whelan, A. and Dunning, D. J. (1982) *Developments in Plastics Technology* 1. Elsevier Applied Science, Barking, Chapter 3.
2 Braun, K. J. and Helmy, H. A. (1979) Single screw extruder developments. Paper at PRI International Conference 'Polymer Extrusion', London.
3 Hind, V. C., Hall, H. B. and Whitehead, K. (1982) *Developments in Plastics Technology* 1. Elsevier Applied Science, Barking, Chapter 5.

# 7 Polymers in telecommunications and power transmission

S. V. WOLFE

## 7.1 Introduction

### 7.1.1 History and background

A major product of both the telecommunications and power transmission industries is cable, a term covering an extremely wide range of design and construction. However, associated with the cable is the necessary wide range of terminal equipment, exchange equipment, domestic equipment and wiring and external plant. All of these components, cable and ancillary equipment, utilise polymeric materials to a large extent. This chapter examines the requirements and use of polymers in the telecommunications and power transmission industry with particular emphasis on polymers in cable. Future developments in the industries are considered, particularly the rapid development of optical fibre transmission systems in telecommunications and the implications of this development in the use of polymeric materials in this field are discussed.

The history of the telecommunications and power transmission industry extends back to well before the beginning of this century. Throughout the development of both industries there has been a prime requirement for an efficient insulating material and indeed, polymeric materials have been used from the very beginning. In the early years of production and development, natural polymers were used. In the power industry, high voltage cables were insulated with paper made from wood pulp and impregnated with oil. In the telecommunications industry, a range of natural polymers have been used. Early 'twisted pair' cables about the turn of the century comprised copper wires insulated with either paper or cotton and twisted together in pairs with numbers of pairs forming the core of the cable which was then sheathed in lead. Condensers (capacitors) were also paper-wound. In submarine telecommunication cables, the natural polymers gutta percha or balata were used. The first trans-atlantic submarine cable was laid as long ago as 1860, and was insulated with gutta-percha. Co-axial telecommunication cable was first considered seriously around 1936. This utilised a central metallic conductor separated from an outer concentric conductor by an insulator. The first co-axial cable utilised acetylated cotton yarn as an insulator and, later, ebonite was also used.

Despite developments in both rubber compounds and synthetic polymers, it took the second world war to really stimulate the use of synthetic polymers in telecommunications with the need for more sophisticated communication systems and the problems with supply of natural rubber products. From 1942 there was a massive increase in the use of both polyethylene and PVC as insulating materials in all types of telecommunication cables. For example, submarine cables insulated with ICI's new polyethylene were used for secure cross-channel communications in war time contracts.

The use of synthetic polymers in medium and high voltage power cables came much later when thermoplastic low density polyethylene was first used in the 1960s. This was rapidly superseded by cross-linked polyethylene (XLPE) and also by cross-linked EPDM compounds, generally termed EPR. Even today, however, it is extremely difficult to produce extruded power cable insulation of sufficient thickness for very high voltage cables (around 275 kV and above) and here oil-impregnated paper insulation is still used.

### 7.1.2 Requirements of polymers in telecommunications and power transmission

The requirements of polymer insulation materials in both power and tele-communication systems have many factors in common. They need to be good general purpose insulators, have good long-term stability (many cable systems are guaranteed for 25 years or more) and be relatively low cost materials. They would generally need to have relatively low dielectric loss, a high volume resistivity, be easily melt processable as well as possessing reasonable mechanical properties. In many applications a low flammability is important.

In any application of any material, however, it is necessary to achieve a balance of the properties required and where necessary to 'tailor' the material. While it is possible to examine some of the differences in require-ments of polymers for telecommunications and for power applications, the ultimate properties will very much depend on the end-use.

Power cables generally operate at considerably higher voltages than telecommunication cables and therefore they require a high electrical break-down strength which does not deteriorate with time. In addition, the conductor of a power cable may run continuously at an elevated temperature and may have an emergency short circuit temperature well in excess of 100°C. Polymers for high voltage applications must therefore be capable of running at continuously elevated temperatures and be able to withstand occasional high temperature excursions.

Telecommunication cables are likely to operate at higher frequencies than power cables; submarine co-axial cable, for example, can operate at up to 45 MHz. For long haul systems such as submarine, it is essential that the cable attenuation is kept to an absolute minimum and, therefore, here the prime requirement is for a material with low dielectric loss even at high frequencies. For thin-wall wire coating, one of the most important requirements is a uniform wall thickness, contaminant-free material capable of being extruded at high rates. Therefore, here, the overriding parameter is good processability to provide a uniform coating capable of withstanding high voltage.

Polymers for optical fibre telecommunication cables often have very different requirements. They are generally not electrically stressed and their

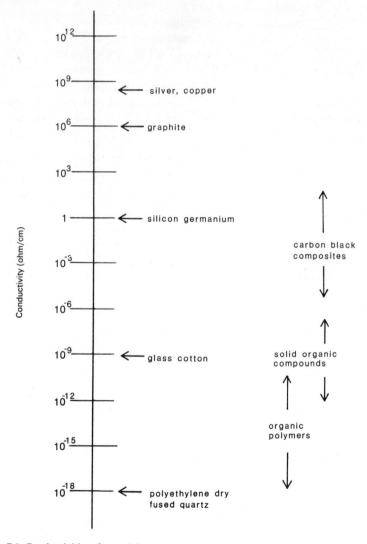

**Figure 7.1** Conductivities of materials.

prime requirement overall is to provide physical protection to the fragile glass fibre as well as providing strength and integrity to the optical fibre package. The special requirements of an optical fibre cable have led to the development of a whole family of polymers cross-linked by UV radiation and these are discussed in more detail later.

## 7.2 Polymers as insulators

### 7.2.1 Measurement of electrical properties

Some of the most important properties of polymers in telecommunications and power transmission are good electrical insulation and low dielectric loss. In this section the background and measurement of conduction and dielectric properties in polymers is discussed.

### 7.2.2 Conductivity and resistivity

Most polymers are good insulators in their unfilled state with materials such as polyethylene, polytetrafluoroethylene and polystyrene being among the best insulators known. Figure 7.1 shows typical conductivities of a range of materials from silver and copper to polyethylene and fused quartz. The conductivity of a material is given by the basic equation

$$\sigma = qn\mu \qquad (7.1)$$

where $q$ is the charge on the carrier, $n$ is the concentration of carriers and $\mu$ is the drift mobility of the carriers. $n$ and $\mu$ are determined by molecular structure and depend on factors such as temperature and applied field. Conduction may be either electronic with electrons and holes as carriers, or ionic with cation and anion carriers. In most polymeric materials, it is difficult to detect any electronic conductivity and most of the conductivity that is observed is due to impurity ions such as catalyst residues, dissociable end groups and degradation products. Therefore, the resistivity $\rho$ (reciprocal of conductivity) of a polymeric material may be significantly improved by purification of the polymer. Polyamides, however, do display pronounced ionic conduction at elevated temperatures which increases by several orders of magnitude between ambient temperature and 100°C. This is probably due to the dissociation of amide groups to give protons with mobility possibly aided by the hydrogen bonding network. Inherently conductive polymers such as polyacetylene and polypyrrole are now more widely researched and some commercial applications are being considered. Polymers that are rendered conducting by the incorporation of carbon black or metal particles are widely used.

The volume resistivity, $\rho_v$, of a material is the resistance between opposite faces of a unit cube and is an important material parameter in polymer insulation. The surface resistivity, $\rho_s$ (the resistance between opposite edges of a unit square), may also be of importance. For high resistivity materials, $\rho_v$ may be measured as a rectangular or cylindrical block of material with electrodes attached to the ends. The volume resistivity, $\rho_v$, is then given by

$$\rho_v = \frac{RA}{l} \tag{7.2}$$

where $R$ is the measured resistance, $A$ is the cross-sectional area and $l$ is the specimen length. For low resistivity materials, $\rho_v$ is best measured on a thin disc of polymer with electrodes painted on either side.

The surface resistivity, $\rho_s$, may be measured using concentric ring electrodes. $\rho_s$ is given by

$$\rho_s = 2\pi R \ln\left(\frac{r_1}{r_2}\right) \tag{7.3}$$

where $r_1$ and $r_2$ are the radii of inner and outer electrodes, respectively.

One problem associated with the measurement of high resistivity materials is leakage currents due, for example, to surface tracking. This may be avoided by use of a guard electrode.

Point probe electrode geometries can also be used to measure volume resistivity, although for high resistivity materials the former method is the more reliable.

### 7.2.3 Electrical breakdown strength

The electrical breakdown strength or dielectric strength of a polymer insulator is the maximum field sustainable by the material and is another property of great significance to both the telecommunications and power industries. This is analogous in many ways to mechanical failure. Failure ultimately depends upon the weakest point in the material. As in mechanical testing, measured dielectric strengths depend on the rate of voltage increase and so tests do not measure an intrinsic value. The best measure of dielectric strength are tests that simulate service performance. In this way, the true breakdown mechanism for a particular system can be probed, whether it is deterministic or based on low-level degradation. Deterministic processes are those where thermodynamically stable processes become locally unstable in response to the applied power in a positive feedback process such as thermal runaway. In low-level degradation, the breakdown characteristics of the material deteriorate with time as in oxidation or water treeing.

However, for comparative materials testing, voltage step or ramp tests on plaques can be valuable. Here, the applied voltage to the sample is increased at a uniform rate until failure occurs. Two major factors must be considered in tests of this kind. Firstly, the field in the sample must be uniform which

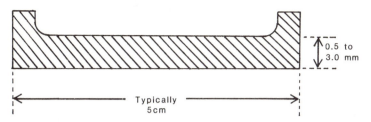

0.5 to
3.0 mm

Typically
5 cm

**Figure 7.2** Rogowski profile.

means that either the sample or the electrode must be specially shaped to avoid stress enhancement at the edges. A commonly used geometric edge profile is that of Rogowski (Figure 7.2). Secondly, the effect of dust contamination on the electrical breakdown strength of polymer mouldings cannot be over-emphasised. The electrical breakdown strength of a moulding can easily be doubled simply by keeping and handling the moulding granules in a dust free environment. There is no question, however, that the electrical breakdown strength of polymer extrudate must be measured in a cable geometry. For large diameter power cables rated at voltages up to 300 kV, this requires large and expensive high voltage test facilities (Figure 7.3). If

**Figure 7.3** A high voltage test laboratory.

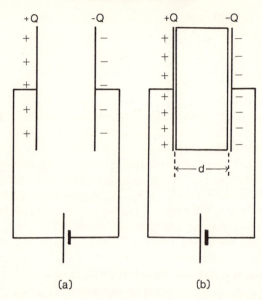

**Figure 7.4** Charges on a parallel plate capacitor with (a) a vacuum and (b) a dielectric medium between the plates.

these are not readily available, scaled down 'model' cables can often yield useful results if they are manufactured under comparable conditions.

### 7.2.4 Capacitance, dielectric loss and cable attenuation

The dielectric properties of polymers are important both in power and telecommunications systems. If we consider the transmission performance of a co-axial cable, the signal attenuation $\alpha$ per unit length of co-axial cable is given by

$$\alpha = A\varepsilon^{1/2}(Bf^{1/2} + 2\pi f \delta) \qquad (7.4)$$

where $A$ and $B$ are constants for a given system, $f$ is the operational frequency, $\varepsilon$ is the relative permittivity or dielectric constant of the insulation material and $\delta$ is the loss angle or power factor of the insulation (and approximates to $\tan \delta$ since $\delta$ is small).

The attenuation is proportional to the square root of the relative permittivity of the insulation, so it is clear that the relative permittivity $\varepsilon$ should be kept as low as possible in co-axial applications. To understand the significance of $\varepsilon$, it is simplest to consider a dielectric in a parallel plate capacitor (Figure 7.4). In a vacuum, the charges per unit area $+Q$ and $-Q$ stored in the plates are directly proportional to the field

$$Q = \varepsilon_0 E \qquad (7.5)$$

where $E$ is the electric field and $\varepsilon_0$ is the permittivity of free space. The vacuum capacitance per unit area of electrode $C_0$ is defined as

$$C_0 = \frac{Q}{V} \qquad (7.6)$$

where $V$ is the applied voltage.

When a dielectric is introduced between the plates of the capacitor, it becomes polarised and at low fields the polarisation is proportional to the field. As a result of the polarisation, more charge will be stored on the capacitor electrodes for the same applied voltage as in vacuum, thereby increasing the capacitance of the system. The ratio of the increased capacitance to the vacuum capacitance is $\varepsilon$, the relative permittivity, and is given by

$$\varepsilon = \frac{C}{C_0} \qquad (7.7)$$

In an alternating field, there will be two components as a result of the polarisation alternating in direction leading to dipolar orientation lagging behind the applied field. The complex dielectric constant $\varepsilon^*$ is given by

$$\varepsilon^* = \varepsilon' - i\varepsilon'' \qquad (7.8)$$

where $\varepsilon'$ relates to the energy stored in a cycle and $\varepsilon''$ relates to the energy lost or dissipated per cycle and is known as the dielectric loss factor. Tan $\delta$, the dielectric loss tangent or dissipation factor, is defined as

$$\tan \delta = \frac{\varepsilon''}{\varepsilon'} \qquad (7.9)$$

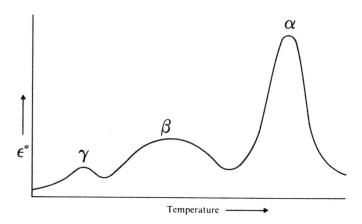

**Figure 7.5** A schematic dielectric loss curve.

In an analogous way to dynamic mechanical analysis, a plot of $\varepsilon''$ as a function of temperature at constant frequency for any polymeric material will reveal peaks associated with molecular transitions within the polymer (Figure 7.5) such as the glass transition and lower order transitions.

There is a relationship between DC conductivity $\sigma$ and $\varepsilon''$

$$\varepsilon'' = \frac{\sigma}{\varepsilon_0 \omega} \tag{7.10}$$

where $\omega$ is the angular frequency. This means that if the polymer has an appreciable conductivity, this will increase the loss factor, particularly at low frequencies.

A whole range of techniques are available for measuring dielectric properties such as the loss factor and the $\tan \delta$, and the technique employed depends to some extent upon the frequency range. At low frequencies, up to around $10^6$ Hz, bridge techniques can be used. These are the most common methods for determining dielectric properties. The equivalent electrical current for a sample is determined at a given frequency by balancing the bridge circuit. The most versatile form for measurement of dielectric properties is the Schering bridge, which can operate from 10 to $10^5$ Hz.

At higher frequencies, between about $10^5$ and $10^8$ Hz, resonance methods are most sensitive. Here the sample is probed by making it part of a resonant circuit. The Hartshorn and Ward method is the most widely used. At frequencies above $10^9$ Hz, wave transmission methods are used which involve establishing standing waves in a waveguide or co-axial line with a closed end and with the dielectric sample filling the space inside to a given distance from the closed end. A more detailed treatment of dielectric measurement techniques is given by Blythe.

Clearly, for any given application, measurement techniques for resistivity, electrical breakdown strength and dielectric properties will be closely specified in the relevant BS, ASTM and other international standards and reference should be made to these, not only for testing techniques, but also for detailed property specifications.

## 7.3 Polymers in telecommunications

We have so far considered general properties and measurement techniques without considering specific polymers in detail. Some specific examples of telecommunications and power transmission are now examined as the best means of illustrating the use of polymers in these applications.

### 7.3.1 Cable materials

Designs of electrical telecommunication cables are extremely diverse with specifications to suit a particular application. However, to generalise in this chapter, it is probably most straightforward to consider cables simplistically as comprising either

(a)  Arrays of polymer coated wires
(b)  Co-axial cable

which are then coated with a sheathing material for mechanical and environmental protection. The insulation, either the wire coating or the co-axial insulation, must have good electrical and mechanical characteristics as previously described. The sheathing material, however, has no such requirement for electrical performance, its main requirements being for chemical and environmental stability, resistance to cracking, good mechanical performance and good processability. Because of the requirement of environmental stability, many sheathing polymers are compounded with a small amount of carbon black for UV stability.

A large proportion of the polymers used in insulation and sheathing are polyethylene and PVC. Table 7.1 shows some typical properties for these materials. PVC has a higher relative permittivity due to its polar structure. For many applications, polyethylene is the ideal polymer. It has excellent

**Table 7.1**  Typical electrical properties of polymers

| Polymer | Volume resistivity (ohm/cm) at 23°C, 50% RH | Relative permittivity (at 1 MHz) | Loss factor (tan $\delta$) (at 1 MHz) | Dielectric strength (kV/mm) (ASTM D149, 0.125 mm sample) |
|---|---|---|---|---|
| Polyethylene (LD) | $>10^{16}$ | 2.2–2.4 | <0.0005 | 18–28 |
| Polyethylene (HD) | $>10^{16}$ | 2.2–2.4 | <0.0003 | >31 |
| EVA | $10^{14}$–$10^{16}$ | 2.6–3.2 | 0.03  –0.05 | ~25 |
| Polypropylene | $10^{17}$ | 2.6–2.7 | <0.0003 | 10–22 |
| Polystyrene | $>10^{13}$ | 2.4–3.1 | 0.0001–0.005 | 20–27 |
| Polyvinylchloride (rigid) | ~$10^{16}$ | 3.0–3.3 | ~0.005 | ~17 |
| Polyvinylchloride (plast) | — | 4  –8 | 0.1  –0.2 | — |
| Nylon 66 | $10^{13}$–$10^{14}$ | 3  –6 | 0.02  –0.06 | 15–19 |
| Nylon 6 | $10^{12}$–$10^{14}$ | 3  –7 | 0.02  –0.12 | 17–20 |
| Polycarbonate | $10^{16}$ | 2.6–3.0 | ~0.1 | 16–17 |
| Noryl™ | $>10^{15}$ | 2.6–2.7 | 0.001  –0.002 | 19–22 |
| Polyetheretherketone | $>10^{16}$ | 3.2–3.3 | 0.003 | 19 |
| Polyetherimide | $10^{17}$ | 3.1 | 0.001 | 23 |
| Polytetrafluoroethylene | $10^{19}$ | 2.1 | 0.0002 | 16–24 |
| Epoxides | $>10^{15}$ | 3  –4 | 0.01  –0.02 | 14–18 |
| Phenol formaldehydes (electrical grades) | $10^{11}$–$10^{14}$ | 4.3–5.4 | 0.01  –0.02 | 10–17 |

electrical properties, it is relatively cheap, easy to process and has a wide range of physical properties depending upon its molecular structure and in particular, its molecular weight and degree of branching. More recently, linear low density polyethylenes have become available for cable extrusion with significant improvement in mechanical properties, particularly the resistance to stress cracking. These materials are essentially copolymers with the comonomer units acting as short chain branches which restrict the degree of crystallisation in a controlled manner. Copolymers containing vinyl acetate (VA) and blends of polyethylene with ethylene vinyl acetate copolymer (EVA) are also being increasingly used for improved stress cracking resistance.

### 7.3.2 Cellular insulation

Polyethylene wire insulation is often produced as a foam or cellular insulation for its good physical and electrical properties, generally using medium or high density polyethylene. Cellular insulation is now generally produced as 'foamskin', with a solid skin surrounding the cellular core. The relative permittivity of foamed insulation has been shown empirically to obey the following relationship

$$\varepsilon = 1 + (\varepsilon_p - 1)V_p \qquad (7.11)$$

where $\varepsilon_p$ is the relative permittivity of the solid polymer and $V_p$ is the volume fraction of polymer with values generally between about 0.55 and 0.7.

Cables of this type generally contain a water blocking material such as petroleum jelly and it is therefore of great importance to ensure that the mechanical and electrical properties are not significantly impaired by absorption of the water blocking material. The 'skin' around the foamed insulation is of significant benefit in preventing absorption.

### 7.3.3 Submarine cable insulation

Submarine cables are based on a co-axial design (although increasingly they are being replaced by optical constructions) and in this application, low density polyethylene comes into its own. Low permittivity and low tan $\delta$ are of paramount importance in this application as is material cost; a typical submarine co-axial system would utilise around 1 tonne of polymer per kilometre. In order to reduce the dielectric loss of the material to an absolute minimum, polar groups are excluded from the material as far as possible. The polyethylene is polymerised under special conditions to minimise contamination by catalyst residues etc., and special antioxidants are used which are symmetrical, the polar groups at either end of the molecule therefore balancing each other. Although most new submarine cable systems are optical, much of the existing international telecommunications network is still based on co-axial systems.

### 7.3.4 Low fire risk materials

While PVC has been, and still is, an important material in cable insulation and sheathing, there is a much greater emphasis today on the use of non-halogenated materials in electrical insulation. An extremely important factor in the selection of insulation and sheathing materials is the flammability, smoke evolution and toxicity of the evolved gases. These are of extreme importance for cable (whether power or telecommunications) to be used for telephone exchanges, underground railway tunnels, oil rigs, shipboard, mines etc. The importance of most of these properties is clear and PVC has been widely used due to its relatively low flammability as a result of the halogen content in its chemical structure. Halogenated flame retardant additives are also used in other polymers to reduce flammability. However, once halogenated materials ignite, the smoke given off on burning is frequently dense and toxic. Gases such as hydrogen chloride given off by burning PVC are extremely corrosive and can seriously damage electrical and electronic equipment in the vicinity of the fire. These problems have led many companies to develop low flammability and low aggressivity materials and cable constructions.

The flammability of a polymeric material is generally gauged in terms of its limiting oxygen index (LOI). This is a measure of the minimum concentration of oxygen, expressed as a volume percentage, in a flowing mixture with nitrogen that will support flaming combustion of a standard test specimen under specified conditions. Another parameter which is also widely used is the critical temperature index (CTI) which is the temperature at which the LOI reduces to 21. Table 7.2 compares the burning behaviour of PVC with that of low density polyethylene and other materials.

The basis of many fire retardant compounds is the incorporation of a high proportion of fire retardant filler into a thermoplastic matrix. The polymer extrudate on the cable is often cross-linked to improve the fire performance still further. The most widely used fire retardant filler is alumina trihydrate.

**Table 7.2** Key properties of insulating materials

| Properties | Noryl™ | Ultem™ | PEEK | Typical PVC | LDPE |
|---|---|---|---|---|---|
| Specific gravity | 1.06 | 1.17 | 1.30 | 1.4 | 0.92 |
| Ultimate tensile strength (MPa) | 40 | 120 | 100 | 20 | 15 |
| Elongation at break (%) | 250 | 150 | 200 | 300 | 500 |
| Limiting oxygen index (%) | 32 | 47 | 38 | 30 | 17 |
| Temperature index (°C) | 320 | 330 | 325 | 220 | N/A |
| Smoke generation | Medium | V. low | V. low | High | Med |
| Relative permittivity | 2.6 | 3.1 | 3.0 | 4 –5 | 2.3 |
| Max. operating temperature (°C) | 100 | 200 | 200 | 100 | 80 |

Between the temperature range 160°–260°C, the material decomposes releasing up to 30% of its weight as water. This decomposition is endothermic thereby reducing the risk of ignition and the water evolved is considered to further suppress ignition and flame spread by absorbing heat and excluding oxygen. For maximum fire retardance, a high level of filler must be incorporated. The thermoplastic should therefore possess a relatively low melt viscosity over a reasonable temperature range and the compounded material should possess reasonable mechanical properties such as flexibility and tensile strength as well as reasonable electrical characteristics. A range of thermoplastics have been employed as the base material, including EVA copolymers and ethylene propylene diene monomer (EPDM) elastomers. Compounds such as these could be used either as insulation or sheathing materials.

Coupled with the development of fire retardant compounds has been the development of fire retardant and high temperature resistant polymers, the so-called 'high performance' polymers. While these generally offer excellent all round physical properties, they tend to be rather expensive (up to around 40 times greater cost than polyethylene) and therefore tend to be reserved for more specialised cable applications. These polymers, such as polyetherether ketone (PEEK), are characterised by a highly aromatic structure imparting thermal stability to the material and consequently a high processing temperature.

Specialised cable applications such as nuclear power stations have additional requirements to good electrical properties and good fire retardant properties. Cables in such environments would be expected to operate even in the event of a loss of coolant accident (LCA) and must therefore be capable of operating after fairly long-term high temperature excursions and after irradiation. Extremely stringent specifications are required for cables in these environments, particularly control cables, and these can be fully satisfied by high performance polymers and careful cable design.

### 7.3.5  Ageing in telecommunication cables

Any cable must be designed not only for good initial performance, but also good long-term performance and therefore, there must be no significant degradation of the polymer over the design lifetime of the cable. Degradation could occur through thermal, oxidative or UV effects, some of which may be accelerated by the presence of copper, which is a problem where a cable has a copper conductor. Most insulation or sheathing materials therefore contain antioxidants, UV stabilisers and copper deactivators as appropriate to the cable design. There is also the possibility of interaction of the polymer with other cable components (petroleum jelly, for example), and it is therefore necessary in any cable to carry out accelerated ageing tests both at elevated temperature and in any potentially aggressive environment such as fuel oils which the cable materials are likely to encounter. For many polymeric materials, a degradation process can be defined by a single temperature-dependent reaction following the Arrhenius equation

$$K = A \exp\left(\frac{-E_a}{kB_T}\right) \qquad (7.12)$$

where $K$ is the reaction rate, $A$ is the frequency factor, $E_a$ is the activation energy for the process, $k$ is Boltzmann's constant and $T$ is the absolute temperature.

If tests are carried out over a range of elevated temperatures, using a criterion such as the time at which the break elongation of a material is reduced by 50%, it is then possible to gain some estimate of the material lifetime at operating temperatures. This assumes that the same degradation mechanism occurs at lower temperatures.

## 7.4 Polymers in power transmission

### 7.4.1 Construction

The construction of a typical medium or high voltage power cable is shown in Figure 7.6. The central conducting core is hard-drawn aluminium wire which possesses high conductivity, mechanical strength and flexibility. In some smaller cables, a solid core may be used which is easier to manufacture but has less flexibility. The thermoplastic insulation (generally PE or EPDM) is extruded and is cross-linked later in the production process to provide better heat stability and a higher continuous operating temperature for the cable.

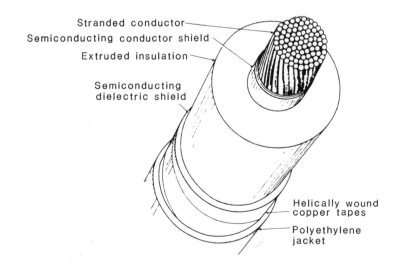

**Figure 7.6** Typical construction of an extruded dielectric cable.

Between the conductor and the insulation and also between the insulation and the outer shield, a layer of semiconducting polymer compound is extruded. This polymer compound bonds to the insulation and helps to prevent void formation between the conductor and the insulation. However, even if small voids are present, the semiconducting compound will take up substantially the same voltage as the adjacent metal, thereby imposing no electrical stress on the void and eliminating the danger of partial discharges within the void which could lead to electrical breakdown. Semiconducting compounds are generally compounds of thermoplastic polymers such as polyolefinic materials with carbon black. They are often cross-linked at the same time as the insulation material. As in telecommunication cables, the sheath material does not have the same requirement for electrical properties as the insulation material and would generally be based on materials such as polyethylene, PVC and polychloroprene. For power cables in enclosed spaces, the same considerations must be given to flammability and burning behaviour as with telecommunication cables.

The insulation material has two prime requirements: a high electrical breakdown strength which is stable over the cable lifetime; and good high temperature performance. The 'intrinsic' calculated breakdown strength of polyethylene, based on its chemical structure, is extremely high (approximately $8.5 \times 10^8$ V/m) at ambient temperature. Although this is never realised in practice, it does imply that very high breakdown strengths should be achievable in a pure and sufficiently stress-free material. To achieve sufficient cleanliness and purity, low density polyethylene for power cable applications is polymerised, transported and processed into the finished cable under completely clean conditions. Even material handling in most power cable factories is carried out under clean, dust-free 'hoods'. This includes the transfer of the polymer to the extruder hopper. To further decrease the risk of contamination, the inner semiconducting layer, the insulation and the outer semiconducting layer are all extruded in essentially one process (triple extrusion) to avoid interfacial particulate contamination. The extrusion rate is slow compared with most telecommunication systems partly due to the need to cross-link the material on-line and partly due to the large insulation thickness, particularly for high voltage cables which can be up to 80–90 mm or more in diameter.

### 7.4.2 Cross-linking

The polyethylene is generally cross-linked in one of two ways: either by peroxide cross-linking at elevated temperatures or by a mechanism involving grafting of silane groups onto the polymer followed by reaction with water. Radiation cross-linking has also been considered. Both methods are widely used. In peroxide cross-linking, a small amount of peroxide (generally dicumyl peroxide) is blended into the polymer after the polymerisation process. This forms a relatively stable material and may be handled and processed as thermoplastic polyethylene providing the extrusion temperature is kept *below* the decomposition temperature of the peroxide. For dicumyl peroxide, it is advisable to keep processing temperatures below 140°C. Once the polymer has been extruded, it may be cross-linked by raising the extrudate temperature to that above the decomposition temperature of the peroxide. Cross-linking then occurs:

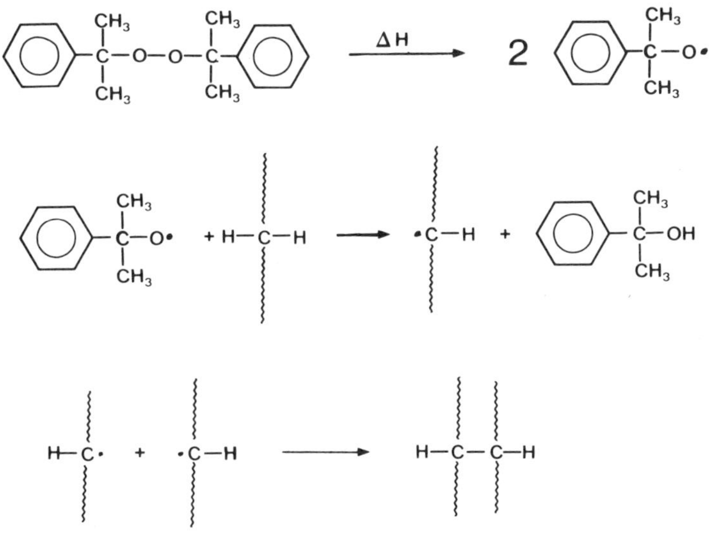

There are by-products of the cross-linking reaction, such as acetophenone, methane and methyl styrene, and in order to avoid these producing voids in the insulation, it is necessary to maintain the molten polymer under some pressure during cross-linking and subsequent cooling. Heat is generally provided for cross-linking by hot dry nitrogen, steam or hot silicone oil.

In silane cross-linking, silane groups are grafted to the polyethylene chain. If the resulting material is kept dry, it can be treated and processed as thermoplastic polyethylene. During extrusion, a catalyst is normally incorporated into the material as masterbatch and the extruded insulation may then be cross-linked by exposure to moisture as in the following scheme.

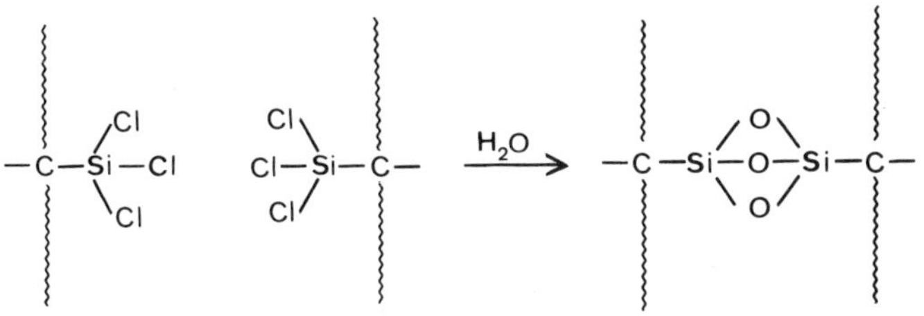

Cross-linking is fairly slow, even at elevated temperatures, and must be carried out as a batch process on drums of cable. Moisture is normally provided by high temperature steam in large 'saunas' or by hot water in large tanks. Under these conditions, cross-linking is effected within the timescale of one to several days. Cross-linking will occur from ambient moisture, although very slowly. This process is not as widely used as the peroxide mechanism for two main reasons: firstly, the cross-linking process is slow and is not feasible for large diameter cables due to the rate at which moisture can penetrate to the centre of the cable; secondly, the silane grafted polymer has a short shelf-life before ambient moisture causes sufficient cross-linking to render the polymer unprocessable. New developments in grafting technology, however, are currently addressing the problem of short shelf-life.

### 7.4.3 Alternatives to XLPE

Developments in ethylene propylene rubber (EPR) and ethylene propylene diene monomer (EPDM) compounds have made them viable alternatives to cross-linked polyethylene (XLPE) in recent years. The EPR and EPDM compound formulations vary considerably, but all are based on a mineral filler content of up to 60%, stabilisers, processing aids, cross-linking agents and small amounts of other additives. The mineral filler is generally a calcined clay which is often silane treated to reduce the water absorption characteristics of the compound. They are generally cross-linked by dicumyl peroxide in a similar way to XLPE although some are silane cross-linked. If ready-compounded, these materials may be slightly more expensive than XLPE. The relative permittivity is also higher due largely to the filler and the measured initial electrical breakdown strength on cable is generally slightly lower than XLPE (the intrinsic breakdown strength is difficult to calculate due to the complex structure). However, there is some evidence that EPR and EPDM compounds exhibit a better long-term performance under voltage stress than XLPE and they are in some cases considered to be less sensitive to low-level contamination than XLPE.

### 7.4.4 Production techniques

The extrusion process for XLPE, EPR and EPDM is slow, partly due to the relatively large cable diameter and consequently longer cooling time, particularly for high voltage rated cables, and partly due to the need for on-line vulcanisation in the case of cross-linking. There could be a danger of the polymer extrudate slumping and the cable insulation becoming eccentric around the conductor unless precautions are taken. Power cable insulation is, therefore, produced either on a vertical extrusion line, a catenary line or on a

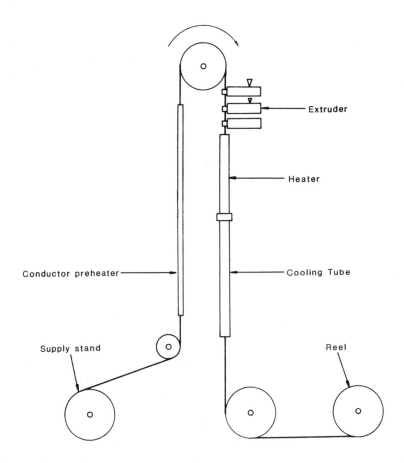

**Figure 7.7** A vertical continuous vulcaniser.

line where the take-up is on a lower level than the extruder. A schematic diagram of a vertical triple extrusion line is shown in Figure 7.7.

### 7.4.5 Ageing in power cable insulation

Many power cables are required to have a 40-year lifetime from installation and indeed, some oil and paper insulated cables are still in operation after 80 years' service. XLPE, EPR and EPDM insulations are subject to the same

**Figure 7.8** A water tree in XLPE insulation. The tree length is about 5 mm.

type of degradation as telecommunication cable insulation. However, due to the relatively high voltage stress applied to the insulation (up to approximately 6 MV/m), two other forms of degradation may also occur. These are termed 'treeing' due to their visible form. The first form of degradation occurs at high electrical stresses in either wet or dry insulation and is termed 'electrical treeing'. The second form occurs at moderate stresses but only in a wet environment and is termed 'water treeing'. Both forms of degradation lead to a reduction in breakdown strength of the insulation and potentially to premature failure of the cable. Considerable accelerated ageing work has been carried out on power cables in an attempt to understand and eliminate this problem. To a large extent this has been achieved in the case of electrical treeing, which generally initiates from points of high field enhancement within the insulation, such as contaminants and voids. With the stringent material handling procedures now employed in power cable technology, the black carbonised tracks which were the characteristic of electrical trees are now much less frequent.

The problem of water treeing, however, still remains something of an enigma despite an enormous amount of research. Water trees comprise small water-filled voids which initiate and spread in a branching formation along the field direction. Figure 7.8 shows a typical water tree in XLPE insulation. Initiation is again from points of high field enhancement but in the case of water trees, growth can only proceed in a wet environment. Part of the growth process is based on an electrochemical mechanism, albeit not fully understood. Many forms of XLPE, some based on linear low density polyethylene and mainly containing 'tree retardant' additives, are reported to be water tree resistant. EPDM and EPR compounds have also been considered as potentially water tree resistant but no definitive solution to the problem has yet been found with the exception of elimination of water from the cable.

Degradation of polymeric power cable insulation can also occur even in the absence of treeing and, as in telecommunication cable insulation, much work must always be carried out in cable designs in order to attempt to predict their ultimate lifetime in service. The Arrhenius relationship is sometimes used to predict power cable lifetime, but more frequently, Weibull statistics are found to be more applicable. In a simplified Weibull function, the static cumulative probability of failure $P_s$ is given by

$$P_s = 1 - \exp(-Dt^a E^b) \qquad (7.13)$$

where $E$ is the constant applied field, and $D$, $a$ and $b$ are constants defining the system. In any static test, that is, one where the time to failure is determined as a function of time at constant applied field, there is always a large degree of scatter which is both inherently and experimentally based. In dynamic tests, where the breakdown field is determined at a constant voltage ramp rate, the resulting data exhibit less scatter. The *dynamic* cumulative probability of failure $P_D$ is given by

$$P_D = 1 - \exp\left[ D\left(\frac{a}{a+b}\right) t^{(a+b)} E^b \right] \qquad (7.14)$$

A plot of cumulative percentage failure versus log (field at breakdown) yields families of curves of gradient $(a+b)$. By constructing a plot of log (rate of field increase) versus characteristic breakdown strength, a straight line plot of gradient $a/(a+b)$ is obtained, enabling the separate determination of $a$ and $b$. For XLPE, $a$ is typically unity, and $b$ is around 6. The determination of the constant parameters enables prediction of the probability of failure of the cable material at any given field and time.

## 7.5  Optical fibre telecommunication cables

### 7.5.1  Introduction

A little over 20 years ago, Charles Kao and George Hockham proposed that optical fibres could be used as the transmission medium for telecommunications. Since then, optical fibre telecommunication cables have become a reality and have replaced conventional cables in an enormous range of applications. The advantages of optical fibre cables is that they are small,

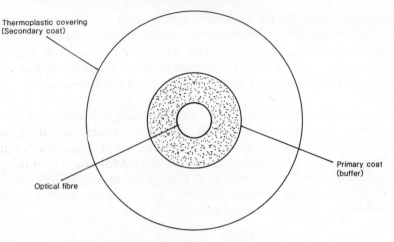

**Figure 7.9** Typical tight fibre cable construction.

light in weight, and size for size, have enormous bandwidth compared with their electrical counterparts. Polymeric materials are essential to the construction of optical fibre telecommunication cables but their requirements in many cases are very different from conventional cables.

Most optical fibre cables are currently based on silica fibre. This is drawn from a glass pre-form and must be coated with a protective polymer layer within seconds of drawing. This protects it from surface crack growth and also acts as a mechanical buffer. A secondary layer is often added at a later

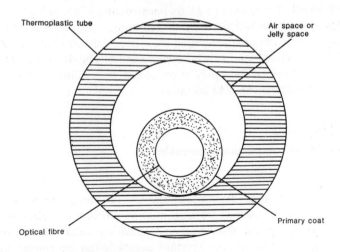

**Figure 7.10** Typical loose tube construction.

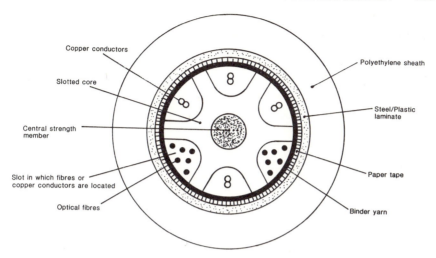

**Figure 7.11** Typical open channel (slotted core) cable construction.

stage for further protection. Coated fibres are the primary units in an optical fibre cable and may be organised to form a variety of cable designs. Figures 7.9, 7.10 and 7.11 show examples of three typical optical fibre cable designs with the use of a variety of polymers in their construction. The polymeric elements in an optical fibre cable may be considered in the following main categories:

(a) Primary coatings;
(b) Encapsulation materials for coated fibres;
(c) Sheathing materials.

### 7.5.2 Primary coatings

The major requirement of primary coatings is essentially physical protection. However, as optical fibres are drawn at a very rapid rate of the order of 1.5 m/s, the coating material must have a low viscosity when applied to the fibre and must solidify very quickly. Fast curing or cross-linkable polymers are in practice the only materials which are adequate for such an application. Some 'hot melt' polymers have been considered but are not used on a wide scale. Early in the development of optical fibre cables, thermally cured primary coatings such as elastomeric silicones were widely used. These have now been largely superseded by UV curable polymers which overcome many problems associated with thermal curing at very rapid rates. The UV curable polymers used are generally acrylic-based polymers such as urethane acrylates, epoxy acrylates or silicone acrylates. Oligomers of these materials are generally viscous and their viscosity is reduced by mixing with reactive diluents. This can give the added advantage of 'tailoring' some of the mechanical properties to cover a very wide range. A photo-initiator is also used to give rapid cross-linking of the polymer on exposure to UV radiation. Many fibres now have dual primary coatings using a soft inner coating and a harder outer coating; both are acrylate based and UV cured. Considerable research into the development of improved UV curable acrylates for optical fibre coating is continuing.

### 7.5.3 Encapsulation materials

Encapsulation materials cover a very wide range of polymers due to wide-ranging construction and requirements. They range from materials for secondary coatings and for loose tubes to slotted core materials. Secondary coating materials for 'tight buffered' cables again need to give the fibre physical protection and, where possible, to impart a longitudinal compression to the fibre. This acts as a safeguard as optical fibre in tension undergoes a form of degradation termed 'static fatigue'. In the case of single fibre cables, it is also possible to consider the use of a high modulus secondary coating, such as a thermotropic liquid crystal backbone polymer, to also act as a strength member. These materials are melt processable copolymers with highly aromatic (and hence very stiff) liquid crystalline groups in the polymer backbone. Some single fibre cables utilise lyotropic liquid crystal polymers such as Kevlar™ as integral strength members. A wide range of secondary coating materials have been employed including nylon 11 and 12, polyester based thermoplastic elastomers and fluorinated polymers for high temperature performance.

Loose tube materials for loose tube cables need to possess a relatively high modulus and good processability. During manufacture, optical fibre is fed into the loose tube at a faster rate than it is being produced so that the optical fibre is laid helically within the tube. To buffer the fibres from each other and from any perturbations on the tube walls, the loose tube is filled with a gel compound similar in composition to the water blocking gels in conventional telecommunication cables. The loose tube material must therefore be compatible with the gel as in conventional cable insulation. Polypropylene has been used for loose tubes but more recently, polyethylene terephthalate and polybutylene terephthalate have become much more widely used.

Slotted core materials in open channel constructions (Figure 7.11) again cover a wide range of materials. As in loose tubes, the inner surface of the slots or channel need to be very smooth to prevent interactions with the fibre and therefore good processability is essential. As in loose tube cables, the channels are filled with a buffering gel and therefore good compatibility is essential. Polyethylene has been widely used in slotted cores but, as in single fibre cables, use of a high modulus polymer could provide an integral slotted core/strength member, thereby dispensing with the need for a central strength member. Thermotropic liquid crystal polymers could again be possible candidates for this.

### 7.5.4 Sheathing materials

Sheathing materials for optical fibre cables have similar requirements to those in conventional telecommunication cables and the same considerations for cable flammability and burning behaviour apply. The main criteria are based on abrasion resistance, cost and long-term performance. Not surprisingly therefore, the largest volume of sheathing material currently used is polyethylene. However, in some respects, the criteria for selection of optical cable sheathing materials are more stringent, as the sheath itself can play an important part in the optical transmission characteristics. If the sheath tends to shrink at low ambient temperatures, or even on solidification after extrusion (sheath retraction), the mechanical forces involved can be transmitted to the optical fibres causing buckling or 'microbending' which in turn causes an increase in attenuation. Thus for optical fibre systems, and particularly long haul systems, sheath retraction must be kept to a minimum.

Although electrical characteristics of sheathing materials are not generally very important, the sheathing material in submarine optical fibre cables has an additional role as insulation. This is because the cable has a dual role of transmitting optical signals and also powering the optical regenerators or repeaters spaced at around 40–100 km throughout the system. These operate in a DC mode at voltages of up to 12 kV, which requires a polymer with excellent insulation characteristics although not necessarily good high frequency properties. This need is currently satisfied by low density polyethylene and medium density polyethylene.

### 7.5.5 Ageing in optical fibre cables

As in any cable, there is always a requirement for long-term testing and lifetime prediction. This is carried out in a similar way to conventional telecommunication cable with respect to polymer materials testing. The long-term mechanical performance of the coated fibres is analysed in terms of Weibull statistics in order to evaluate the static fatigue performance. However, there is one additional criterion which must be considered when evaluating potential degradation in optical cables and that is the extent to which individual cable components and combinations of cable components evolve hydrogen. Hydrogen diffuses into silica fibres and can interact with the glass matrix to give rise to significantly increased optical attenuation. This is of particular importance in long haul enclosed systems, such as submarine cables, where there is no opportunity for hydrogen to diffuse out of the cable.

In some cases it is possible to optimise the cable design or use polymer additives such as certain antioxidants to reduce hydrogen evolution.

### 7.5.6  Future trends in optical fibre cables

All of the foregoing discussion relates to cabling of silica optical fibres. There are currently developments in optical fibres which are based on polymers such as polymethylmethacrylate rather than silica although it is unlikely that they will be used in telecommunications to any great extent in the near future, due to their high optical attenuation (80 dB/km) compared with approximately 0.1 dB/km for silica). Developments in new glasses for optical materials of lower loss than silica may mean that improved optical fibre coating materials may need to be developed.

## 7.6  Optically non-linear polymers in telecommunications

In order to switch an optical signal, the optical signal must first be converted, switched electronically and then reconverted to an optical signal. This is clearly not an efficient process and has led researchers in recent years to investigate means of carrying out a variety of operations, such as switching, entirely optically. This can be done by materials that possess non-linear optical properties, that is, the optical properties of the material change in a non-linear manner as a function of incident light intensity. This has become an important field of research.

Initial work concentrated on crystalline inorganic materials such as lithium niobate, gallium arsenide and gallium aluminium arsenide. In recent years, potentially highly non-linear organic and polymeric materials have become widely researched worldwide as the scope of these materials goes beyond telecommunications. It is not possible to begin to review the work that has been carried out here but merely to outline the basis of the research and indicate the types of materials that are being studied today.

The molecular polarisation $P$ induced by an electric field $E$ is given by a power series

$$P = \alpha E + \beta E^2 + \gamma E^3 \ldots \tag{7.15}$$

where $\alpha$ is the polarisability and $\beta$, $\gamma$ etc. are the hyperpolarisabilities. $\alpha$, $\beta$ and $\gamma$ are all *molecular* parameters. Materials with large non-linear coefficients, $\beta$ and $\gamma$, can exhibit a wide range of useful properties. Such materials must be polar and should preferably exhibit strong absorption at low frequencies. If a high second-order coefficient is required in the bulk material, then any crystallisation in the material should be non-centrosymmetric otherwise the second-order coefficient will become zero. Additionally, a high degree of conjugation will generally enhance non-linearity.

Non-linear polymers that have been considered for optical applications can be broadly divided into two classes: inherently non-linear polymers; and guest/host systems. Inherently non-linear polymers are based on highly conjugated materials such as polydiacetylenes. Guest/host systems were originally envisaged as simple blends of non-linear organic compounds with a glassy polymer. However, as the bulk non-linearity of the material is proportional to the number of contributory molecules per unit volume, it became clear that solubility and other limitations in simple blends could restrict the magnitude of the non-linearity attainable. Guest/host systems have therefore evolved towards chemically grafted copolymers with the non-linear group generally attached as a side chain to the polymer backbone. Side chain liquid crystal polymers are becoming increasingly widely studied in this context.

## 7.7 Conclusions

Although polymers have been used in telecommunications and power transmission since before the beginning of this century, new developments are still taking place today, both in cable and system construction and in the polymers themselves. The whole range of polymer properties are important in these developments, from mechanical performance to electrical behaviour and more recently to optical properties. With the advent of optical fibre technology, polymer development has increased at a tremendous rate and probably most rapidly in the field of opto-electronics and non-linear optics. Some of the developments currently taking place in this area are as exciting as any developments in polymer engineering so far and when successful, will revolutionise our approach to communications and information technology.

## Further reading

Young, P. (1983) *Power of Speech.* George Allen & Unwin, London.
Blythe, A. R. (1979) *Electrical Properties of Polymers.* Cambridge University Press, Cambridge.
Shaw, M. T. and Shaw, S. H. (1984) *IEEE Trans. Electr. Insul.*, **19**, 419.
Various Authors (1986) Proc. 2nd Int. Conference on Power Cables on Accessories, London.
Stevens, G. C. (ed.) (1988) *Recent Advances in the Morphology of Polymeric Cable Insulation.* P. Peregrinus Press, UK.
Various Authors (1986) Proc. 4th Int. Conference on Plastics in Telecommunications, London.

# Index